The Wired City

A History of the Telephone in Edmonton

by Margaret Stinson

To Queen Storytime
Thank you for being
a dedicated
"Kids-on-the-Fringe"
Performer

Boss

ii

This book is dedicated to all 'edmonton telephones' employees, past, present and future, whose contribution and effort has helped mold and sustain 'edmonton telephones'.

G. K. Foster,
General Manager
'edmonton telephones'

edmonton telephones
Owned And Operated
by the City of Edmonton

January 1, 1905 to January 1, 1980
75 years a city utility

About the Author

Margaret Stinson is a graduate of the University of Regina, Arts Program, and the University of Western Ontario post-graduate course in Journalism. She has worked in traffic and continuity in radio and television; worked as a photo-journalist for a weekly paper, conducted short term research and writing projects for associations and private researchers; and written a history of the Edmonton Kinsmen Club. Margaret lives in Spruce Grove with her husband and son.

Contents

Necessity is the Mother of Invention

During the years that Alexander Graham Bell of Boston was displaying his marvelous new invention at the fairs and exhibitions in the United States, the small community of Edmonton, North-West Territories, was beginning to break its close ties with the Hudson's Bay Company. The glorious and romantic days of Fort Edmonton, home of fur traders and Indians, were coming to an end as more and more settlers began to homestead on the banks of the Saskatchewan River. Farmers, merchants and fortune seekers arrived daily, horse or oxen-drawn carts piled high with tools and household goods. Houses, churches and stores sprang up and spread like wild oats. The men and women who sowed the seeds of this new community were true pioneers. They were men and women of action and initiative, with minds open to new ways in a new land.

By 1879, Edmonton was an enterprising village of 200 people, but a village in a vacuum. The only means of communication with the outside world, other than the newsy visitor on horseback, was the mail. And the mail was not only undependable, but unbearably slow.

The original mail carrier, or his horse, must have been a nature lover, for the mail route meandered past all the local sights. In that year, a letter mailed in Edmonton for Fort McLeod went first to Battleford, then to Cypress, then to Benton in Montana, then finally to McLeod. It travelled over 650 miles out of its way.

Another communication device — the telegraph — was rarely used by the villagers, since in 1879 the last relay point of the Government Telegraph Line was at Hay Lakes, thirty miles from Edmonton. The telegraph line itself extended west of Hay Lakes, and in 1876 terminated at a point eighteen miles south of Edmonton. The government apparently could not see any point in extending the line all the way to Edmonton, an unimportant northern fur trading post, even though Richard Fuller, the government contractor for the Hay Lakes-Battleford segment of the line, was the only contractor to build his portion on schedule and at a reasonable cost.

Hay Lakes was not an official telegraph office, but the operator, James McKernan, did send and receive messages, chiefly for government officials and the police force. James McKernan had moved west with his brother Robert to take charge of the Hay Lakes telegraph line. In 1879, McKernan decided to leave his job as operator. Mr. Fuller, the contractor, then hired an Ottawa man, Alexander Taylor, who later introduced the telephone to Alberta and became the driving force behind Edmonton's telephone system.

James McKernan continued to work on the line in repair, construction, and occasionally as operator. In 1881 he moved northeast of Edmonton to farm. His brother Robert had moved shortly before and was farming on the south side of the river, beside McKernan Lake. Later, Robert became proprietor of the Strathcona Hotel.

In 1878 Edmontonians petitioned the government to extend the telegraph line to Edmonton. In order to interest the government in the plan they offered to bear part of the expense. A total of $187 was raised for that purpose. Fuller promised to supply the wire and other materials, and poles supplied by the Hudson's Bay Company would be erected by local volunteer labour. The government could hardly refuse a project that was self-supporting, so work on the telegraph extension to Edmonton began under the direction of James McKernan.

Alex Taylor continued to operate the Hay Lakes station until December 19, 1879, the day the new Edmonton telegraph office opened. The building, owned by John Walter, was located on the flats across the river from the Fort which was situated on the present Legislature grounds. The office remained there until the following spring when it was moved inside the walls of Fort Edmonton.

When Alex Taylor moved to Edmonton as telegraph operator, James McKernan resumed full charge of the Hay Lakes post. In the spring of 1881, Taylor left his post in order to farm. The telegraph business must have been more interesting than his life as a farmer, for in April of 1882 he returned to the Edmonton telegraph office. He worked there as operator until 1893.

In the interim, George S. Wood was operator. Later, his travels took him east, and in General Middleton's account of the North-West Campaign of 1885, Wood was stated to have shown great pluck and professional ability.

Edmonton's communications future looked bright early in 1880, but the citizens soon discovered Murphy's Law: Whatever can go wrong, will! Problems with the new telegraph line caused frequent communication breakdowns. Townspeople were annoyed and disappointed by the many delays.

The line got off to a weak start because the wire used was substandard. It would snap in a brisk wind, and in winter would sag and break from the weight of the accumulated snow. As well as the hard hand of nature, native animals caused many breakdowns. The Alberta bison, being deprived of adornment for generations, put telegraph wire high on the list of fashionable attire. The fashion soon spread from Edmonton to Winnipeg and became a frequent reason for downed wires. Raging prairie fires were another frequent hazard that destroyed poles and wires. Then there was the occasional belligerent person who deliberately cut the wires.

When the telegraph office opened in Edmonton, Alexander Taylor secured the services of a T. Walsh of Winnipeg as a news correspondent. Twice a week Walsh would wire Taylor the latest national and international news stories. The news was then copied out by Taylor and John Alexander Mitchell. According to one version of the tale, five copies were made: one for Bishop Grandin of St. Albert; one for the chief factor of the Hudson's Bay Company; one for the mounted police commandant at Fort Saskatchewan; one for the public, to be posted as a bulletin on the door of the Hudson's Bay

Company store; and a file copy. This news circular was very popular with the citizens of Edmonton.

This arrangement worked well until the spring of 1880 when Gladstone was returned to power in the British Parliament. Walsh, in his enthusiastic report on the election, sent along the line a barrage of Welsh names that were difficult to spell and hard to copy. Just as Taylor and Mitchell were developing writer's cramp, Frank Oliver happened to drop into the office.

Oliver, a local merchant, had previously been a newspaperman with the *Winnipeg Free Press*. Taylor suggested half-jokingly that Oliver should start a newspaper, to relieve Taylor of his job of bringing the news to the public. Oliver agreed. Not only would the paper provide news from the outside world, it could also be used for local news and advertisements. A partnership between Taylor and Oliver was born with net assets totalling $21, the amount needed to buy a $4 press and pay for the duty and shipping charges from Philadelphia to Winnipeg.

That summer Oliver travelled to Winnipeg, picked up the 200 pound miniature press and secured some type from Mr. Luxton of the *Free Press*. On his return journey, Oliver and his two companions had some difficulty crossing the South Saskatchewan River. One of the oxen slipped in the mud or stepped in a hole, the wagon was overturned and the contents fell into the water. Everything was retrieved except the box containing the banner type. Not willing to delay the introduction of the paper because of lack of headline type, the enterprising Taylor got a piece of dry birch and with his jack-knife carved the words, "The Bulletin." The presses rolled out the first edition of the first Alberta newspaper on December 6, 1880. The birch heading was used for several issues until large type was donated by Mr. Laurie of the *Saskatchewan Herald*.

Mr. Taylor stayed in the newspaper business until 1881 when he left city life to become a farmer, but the ties between Taylor and Oliver weren't broken. In subsequent years Taylor was remembered with affection by the paper. The *Bulletin* would describe him as "the gentlemanly meteorological observer," and faithfully report on his assorted enterprises. Later, when Oliver went to Ottawa and became Minister of the Interior, his daughter frequently entertained Taylor's daughter Eleanor while she was attending school in the east.

The tiny paper was effective in drawing attention to the western community. Even though many articles were inconsequential and unsophisticated, the lofty easterners said it was quite professional for an outpost like Edmonton. The effect was often small-town and humorous, but an undercurrent of pride was always there, as can be seen in the following article:

We don't like to mention it, but quite a number of the citizens of Edmonton and vicinity were more or less — (principally more) drunk on Christmas Eve and Day. They should not set such a bad example, as it may be followed by the residents of Battleford, Winnipeg, Montreal and other suburban districts.

There was no question of that writer's faith in the future of the town, and if any outsider dared to question that prosperous future, the inhabitants were indignant. An incident happened in the spring of '82 which ruffled the feathers of the townspeople. Edmonton was looking for a man to replace the late Dr. Verey, and a resident of another town was recommended and approached to accept the position. The individual in question had the colossal nerve to ask for a guaranteed income of $2000 a year. The consensus was that accepting such conditions would be wrong "not that there is any doubt about the practice amounting to the sum of the guarantee required, but because there is no necessity for such a guarantee, and because a guarantee would be wrong in principle."

Edmontonians were having a hard enough time with communications; they didn't need the added insult of professional men insinuating that Edmonton may not be able to provide them with a livelihood.

The telegraph line was down so much of the time, it was a wonder that any messages got past Battleford. The resulting poor telegraph communications, together with the inadequate mail service, was costing the local businessmen a considerable amount in lost revenue.

One of the concerned town boosters, Alex Taylor, was in a position to know the exact state of affairs with regard to communications. Telegraphs, to be sure, were a good means of sending and receiving messages, but only if the line was in good repair. Being an entrepreneur and scientist at heart, Taylor began to look for other ways of sending messages. Taylor had heard about the telephone, and no doubt he did some daydreaming about the possibilities of Alexander Graham Bell's invention.

Winnipeg had a telephone exchange of some 110 subscribers by the spring of '83. The same year it was reported that a telephone wire was being placed in the residence of Governor Dewdney in Regina. Phones were also placed in the Regina CPR station, in the town offices of the mounted police, and the Royal Hotel.

Well, if Regina could have a telephone system, why not

Edmonton? Taylor wasn't the only person who felt that way. Soon a group of civic-minded individuals got together and approached the Bell Telephone Company in Winnipeg with the idea of setting up a local system. The answer Edmonton received was not at all satisfactory. The Bell agent in Winnipeg, Frank Walsh, apparently felt that Edmonton was much too tiny for Bell to even consider setting up a system. He did add though, that when Edmonton was larger Bell would reconsider the request and see if something could be done for the western frontier town. If that was the attitude Bell was going to take, Edmonton would build its own system! In the meantime, however, the villagers would have to rely on the telegraph and the mail.

The line was in its usual state — down — and poor Mr. McKay, the chief repairer, slept more often out on the bald prairie than he did in his own bed. He was constantly off to Grizzly Bear Coulee, or to some other point east, to fix the lines. Something just had to be done about the telegraph. Once again it was Alex Taylor who came up with an idea.

Taylor contacted Hartley Gisborne, the District Superintendent of Telegraphs, and suggested that the route be changed. The new route would leave the old line at the point at which it crossed the Victoria Trail, and come into Edmonton by way of Beaver Lake and Fort Saskatchewan. Although the route would be longer, it would be easier to keep in working order and would also furnish telegraphic communication to Beaver Lake and Fort Saskatchewan. The idea had been discussed with the people of Fort Saskatchewan, who had offered to share expenses with the government. Hartley replied that the government would probably supply the wire if the people supplied the poles.

Whether it was on his son's suggestion or not, Fred Gisborne, the Superintendent of the Government Telegraph and Signal Service, intended to pay the west a visit in the fall. The villagers looked forward to that visit, optimistic that once the state of affairs was observed firsthand by the elder Gisborne, Edmonton would not be long in getting an improved service.

While Gisborne was visiting the west, the citizens raised the possibility of receiving some aid from the government in constructing a telephone service. Many discussions were held on telegraph and telephone facilities, and Gisborne returned east with some definite proposals. In his report to Parliament he made some observations and suggestions.

He made the following comment about the situation in Edmonton:

> . . . the telegraph station (had) lately been removed from an old and inconvenient room in the Hudson's Bay Fort to a new building in a more central situation, and the operator, Mr. Taylor, is of the opinion that the station will be more self-supporting when a good and reliable line has been constucted. As far as practicable (the station being destitute of almost every necessary appliance for maintenance until my visit when such requirements were promptly furnished) the line will be put in order for winter use by two or three active men whom I provided with a wagon, pair of horses, etc.

In Fort Saskatchewan he found that "this small but thriving community offered to supply good spruce and hacmatack (tamarack) poles, an office rent free, and an operator upon the usual commission agreement, if the government would extend the telegraph line from Edmonton, distant eighteen miles, to the settlement."

He found a similar situation in St. Albert, where "here also the inhabitants were anxious to have telegraphic or telephonic connection with Edmonton, and they volunteered to provide good spruce or hacmatack poles free of cost if the Government will construct a short nine mile line to their settlement."

Also included in his report was a proposal to construct a telegraph line from Edmonton to Calgary.

The report was submitted; Edmonton would have to wait and see what the government would do about Gisborne's proposals. But the telegraph network would surely be improved and there was even a possibility that Edmonton would have telephonic connections with St. Albert.

The Seeds are Sown

The year 1884 looked promising for the village of Edmonton. The previous autumn the railroad had been built to Calgary, and was quick to show its many benefits. Before the appearance of the iron rail in Alberta, goods were hauled by cart from the continuously advancing railhead. Travel by cart was jarring and painfully slow. Goods frequently arrived too battered to be offered for sale. Fall stocks wouldn't arrive until spring; merchandise ordered for spring wouldn't arrive until fall; and transportation costs were high — nine cents a pound via cart from Winnipeg to Edmonton.

With the railhead at Calgary, freight rates dropped to about five cents a pound, there was little damage, and stock arrived on time.

Merchandise could be ordered over the telegraph and the goods would be shipped promptly any time of the year. Merchants could now offer Edmontonians a greater variety of goods for a lower price. Cotton was 10 to 20 cents a yard, cheese was 30 to 40 cents a pound, and myrtle navy tobacco could be had for 75 cents a tin. Now Edmontonians could enjoy the luxury of fresh apples at 25 cents a pound.

That year there was also much talk about the latest geological survey of Eddmonton and district. In northern Alberta, petroleum was found along the Athabasca River. The 150-foot sandstone cliffs were saturated with it, and it was believed that the oil sands extended across a large part of the region between the Athabasca and Peace Rivers. Petroleum was also found on the MacKenzie River near Fort Simpson.

It wouldn't be long before that vast resource of petroleum would beckon the mining companies. Edmonton was the gateway to that northern reserve of wealth, so the little village of Edmonton could see its future as a prosperous city. The time was ripe for Edmonton to be incorporated as a town.

Calgary was already booming. One day in January, 7000 lots were sold for about $350 each. It would not be long before Edmonton would experience — in all likelihood — a larger land boom.

In all the excitement and talk of prosperity, the telegraph was operating as usual — infrequently. Alex Taylor, in addition to his job as telegraph operator, found time for many other interests and activities.

Shortly after he returned to Edmonton, the townspeople were concerned with establishing a cemetery, since, according to the local paper, "although our population is yet small, and climate exceptionally healthy, people will die eventually even here." Taylor was one of the moving forces in organizing the citizens to action, and in a short time a cemetery company was formed. Taylor was one of the owners of the company and a member of the board of directors for many years.

Although Taylor had decided that farming wasn't his forte, he still maintained a lively interest in agriculture. He was a member of the Edmonton Agricultural Society and held executive posts in that organization. He was the main instigator when the society acquired a piece of land to hold agricultural exhibitions. He turned detective, tracking down the identity of a type of giant rye or goose wheat which grew around Edmonton. Determined to find out what the plant was, and whether it had any value, he wrote to various agricultural publications for an answer. The *Prairie Farmer* obliged

Mr. Taylor, informing him that the prolific Polish wheat, or *Triticum polanicum*, unfortunately had no commercial value.

Alex Taylor was also the official weather observer and lightning manipulator for Edmonton. Each week a small section of the local paper was reserved for Taylor's meteorological report, which contained the weekly high and low temperatures, precipitation amounts, and wind velocities.

Being the meteorological observer wasn't as easy as it sounded. In order to obtain the speed and direction of the wind, Taylor had to climb a long, precariously positioned ladder on the telegraph building — a situation which wasn't rectified until the spring of '87. At that time, the combination meteorological station and telegraph office received a long shaft anemometer and windmill vane which enabled readings to be taken from two dial plates attached to the inside wall of the office.

Taylor was also something of an amateur astronomer. In February of '83, Venus was to make her way across the heavens and Taylor made elaborate preparations to observe the phenomenon. He obviously miscalculated for he discovered, just as he was to observe the event, that the transit of Venus had taken place the week before. The *Bulletin* editor wasn't adverse to having a little fun at his friend's expense, and the mistake was broadcast throughout the town. Although not referred to by name, Taylor is easily recognizable as the "gentlemanly meteorological observer, who also manipulates the lightning, or a sufficient proportion thereof."

In the fall of that year, it was again Alex Taylor who came to the rescue after the paper implored the good citizens of the town to come up with a solution to the following problem:

Owing to the great difference in time as shown by the various time pieces in town, people stray into church at all hours. It is an uncommon thing to hear of an engagement being kept owing to the same cause. Can someone propose a remedy?

Undaunted by the Venus episode, Taylor came forth with another of his brilliant schemes. The remedy was simple. First, adopt Railway Standard Time. Then, (for a small subscription to cover the cost of powder) the telegraph operator would fire a small cannon at noon. The cannon was generously loaned for the purpose by Mr. J. McDougall of the Hudson's Bay Company. This plan met with the approval of the townspeople, and in January of the next year it was put into effect with the result, as reported by the *Bulletin*:

The cannon was fired by the gentlemanly telegraph operator and meteorological observer at noon on Saturday, Monday, Tuesday, and Wednesday, but without a satisfactory amount of success until Wednesday, when the report was heard all over town.

Unfortunately Alex wasn't an expert on warfare, but with great tenacity he eventually achieved the desired goal. On the first try he fired the cannon high into the air, with the result that it was heard very clearly two miles away, but wasn't heard within the town limits. Next, he fired into the ground, which didn't work because the powder was poor and the charge insufficient. On Wednesday however, he used good powder, doubled the amount and the resulting explosion was heard distinctly by the townspeople. In March, the cannon was still being fired but apparently not generally heard, so eventually this service was terminated.

In 1884 tricycles were first seen, and became the rage of the younger set. Adults took to wearing green goggles — perhaps to scare off demon drivers.

Telegraph networks in the west were improving. The visit of Fred Gisborne the previous fall had been successful, for a month after his departure a quantity of supplies for the Edmonton telegraph office and the proposed offices at Fort Saskatchewan and Victoria were sent. By the beginning of February, the necessary appropriations were approved for new telegraph lines from Calgary to Edmonton, and from Edmonton to Fort Saskatchewan and St. Albert. The best news of all was that the predictably unreliable line to Battleford was to be abandoned as soon as the Calgary to Edmonton line was completed.

Supplies arrived at the Edmonton telegraph office. It received a fifteen-day clock, a barrel of blue stone, and other materials.

A week later spirits were dashed when a message came to the effect that the Edmonton telegraph lines wasn't altogether approved in Parliament. The expense was cut so much in fact, that it appeared unlikely that anything could be done on the limited budget that Parliament had approved. Fred Gisborne did suggest though, that if the people would offer to furnish the poles between Red Deer and Edmonton, he would have a better chance of convincing Parliament to go ahead with the construction.

The ploy wasn't successful, and Parliament turned down the Calgary-Edmonton telegraph line. Some provision for better telegraph communication was made, however, when the government allocated $8,000 for major repairs to the Battleford-Edmonton line. Also included in the estimates for the fiscal year ending June 1885 were allocations of $1,350 for the Edmonton-Fort Saskatchewan line (poles furnished free of cost to the government) and $675 for the St. Albert-Edmonton line.

That summer the Battleford-Edmonton line underwent a major overhaul, with good results. Telegraphic communication in Edmonton was better than it had been for three years.

In May, construction on the St. Albert-Edmonton line was approved. This was great news for Alex Taylor. If construction progressed swiftly, perhaps he would have telephone communication with St. Albert by Christmas. Taylor ordered two telephones from a firm in London, England then made arrangements with W. McKenny of St. Albert to become the keeper of the telephone in that community.

The guardian of the first phone in St. Albert was also one of the more prominent men in the Edmonton district. H. W. McKenny was born in Ontario in 1848 and came to Edmonton in 1875. He was, at various times, postmaster, police magistrate and chairman of the school board in St. Albert. He also held the positions of license commissioner and secretary-treasurer of the first agricultural society in his district. He was a fluent writer and wrote prose and verse for a number of publications. After he retired from business in 1903, he was elected to the Alberta Legislature as the member from Pembina. McKenny was the Justice of the Peace in St. Albert and was a member of the Edmonton and Canada Clubs.

While McKenny was busy planning construction of his new combination store, dwelling and telephone office, to be located on the south side of the Sturgeon River Bridge, the telephones were making the long journey across the ocean on their way to Edmonton.

The poles for the telegraph-telephone line were put up in the fall and the McKenny building was completed shortly after.

The poles were of tamarac and spruce, peeled, 21 feet long, five inches in diameter at the top end, and set four feet in the ground. There were 32 poles to the mile, and with a price tag of 50 cents per pole, the total cost was about $200. The wire was extra heavy gauge and the insulators were porcelain with oak brackets that screwed on.

The telephones arrived in Edmonton in December, were installed, tested and found in order. Everyone in town was excited at the prospect of being able to talk to someone nine miles away. McKenny's store and Taylor's telegraph office were crowded with people eager to listen to the voice coming over the wire. The telephone was amazing — not only could the operator hear the voice clearly, but everyone else in the room could hear the conversation.

The first official telephone conversation in Alberta took place on January 3, 1885, and the *Bulletin* recorded the momentus event for posterity:

Edmonton, 3 January, 1885. Reverend Father Leduc, St. Albert. We wish you all a very happy new year. Alex Taylor. St. Albert. 3 January, 1885. Edmonton. The people of St. Albert congratulate the people of Edmonton on telephone communication being established between two places, and wish the clergy and people a happy new year. Narcisse St. Jean, Chairman.

At the time, the telephone was a novelty, not an important means of communication. It was fun listening to the sounds coming through the device. At the Edmonton end of the line, listeners could hear meat frying in McKenny's kitchen, and the scratchings of the pens could be heard at either end while the operators took down messages.

Although even the most progressive mind couldn't have imagined the significant impact that the telphone would have on society, the Edmonton citizens of 1885 still felt very proud that the first telephone communication in Alberta had taken place in their community. They were one up on Calgary!

In February a communication came over the wires which led citizens to believe that justice eventually catches up with those of erring ways — the Bell Telephone Company. The Bell Company was unpopular after their Winnipeg representative said that Edmonton was much too insignificant to require a telephone exchange, and the people were not quick to forget. Therefore news of a misfortune befalling Bell did not bring sympathy from the people of the village. The Minister of Agriculture had voided the company's patent in Canada because it had imported the patented articles after twelve months from the date of the patent. It was also stated that Bell had not manufactured in Canada such articles to the extent required by law.

The concerns of the townspeople soon turned to more serious matters. There were uprisings among Indians and Métis in Saskatchewan, and it wasn't long before there was trouble in Alberta as well. On March 27, 1885, a message came through that the Métis had killed ten Royal North West Mounted Police at Duck Lake. Then the telegraph line went silent. Rumors started that Louis Riel had sent letters to Alberta Indians urging them to rebel! Fear mounted and people felt that an Indian attack was imminent.

When news of the Saddle Lake disturbance reached Edmonton, town meetings were called. What could Edmonton do in the case of an Indian attack? Captain Griesbach of the Fort Saskatchewan RNWMP detachment was summoned. He immediately dispatched a few constables to Edmonton, enlisted some local men and issued them arms.

On Saturday, April 11, a rumor circulated, stating that inhabitants of Fort Saskatchewan had been massacred. In the resulting panic many Edmontonians deserted their homes, certain the same fate awaited them if they didn't reach the protecting walls of Fort Edmonton. The following day the report proved erroneous, and as word came that the Alberta Field Force was on its way from Calgary, the people returned to their homes. A great loss was incurred by some people, who in their confusion had turned their cattle loose.

A more intangible loss was a result of Saturday's activities. Since the rumor had been conveyed by telephone from St. Albert, perhaps Mr. McKenny felt partially responsible for the chaos. In any event, his faith in the value of the instrument evaporated, for a few days later the following article appeared in the paper:

The St. Albert telephone has been replaced by a telegraph instrument. Mr. Taylor offers to place the telephone in town if the people will provide the necessary poles.

Alex Taylor didn't receive many requests for the instrument, so he took time to concentrate on more important things. He moved to J. A. MacDougall's old house and got ready to welcome his new bride — Harriet Thomasina Marsh, daughter of Archdeacon Marsh of London, Ontario. Shortly after his wedding of July 29, Taylor was appointed returning officer for the North-West Territories Council elections. He then ran a branch telegraph to his new home.

By November, Taylor's long-standing offer was accepted by the Mission fathers in St. Albert. The telephone was returned to St. Albert and telephonic communication was again established between the two communities.

In the meantime, the Indian and Métis uprising had been suppressed and Louis Riel was apprehended and hanged November 18 at Regina.

In later years Frank Oliver remembered the night early in April, just previous to the rumored Fort Saskatchewan massacre. It was the night the Indian drums were silenced forever. It was the beginning of a new era in the history of Edmonton.

'86 to '90, Slow but Steady

~

The four years from 1886 to 1980 was a period of slow but steady expansion for the telephone system in Edmonton. The only line in use at the beginning of this period was the one from the Edmonton telegraph office to the Catholic mission in St. Albert, but by the end of 1889 nineteen subscribers were tied into the system.

Telegraph service was also expanded in the district. Early in 1886 there was a call for tenders for a telegraph line to Fort Saskatchewan, and by March 15 the poles were in position. By August, construction on the line to Victoria (now called Pakan) was completed. In the fall, a new telegraph office was built adjacent to Alex Taylor's home on Fourth Street. At the end of December the offices in Victoria and Fort Saskatchewan were officially opened. The rate to Fort Saskatchewan from Edmonton and St. Albert was 25 cents for 10 words and two cents for each additional word.

By the summer of '87 the line to Battleford, which had operated successfully all the previous summer, again fell into disrepute. The poles were rotten; renovations would be useless; the entire line would have to be replaced.

During '86, playing checkers over the telegraph line regained its popularity as a pastime, but when the line to Battleford was pronounced dead in '87 the checker players joined other Edmontonians in the latest fad to hit the community — rifle practice.

With a halt to telegraphic news, Edmonton was once more isolated. Local incidents gained prominence and in order to fill the pages of the local paper, even the most trivial happenings were reported — from the blooming of rosebushes to a catastrophe that befell one of the animals belonging to Edmonton's future first mayor. It seems that one day one of Matt MacCaulay's pigs fell sixty-five feet down the stable well. Fortunately someone witnessed the accident and swift action saved porky from an untimely end.

That summer the repair crew got working, and by winter of '87 the telegraph was again open and outside news once again reached Edmonton. Soon after, Edmonton gained direct telegraphic communication with Qu'Appelle.

During this period, Alex Taylor was still active in the community. Besides being official meteorological observer, lightning manipulator and telegraph operator, he took a turn at being the president of the literary club, and remained a director of the cemetery company. Because of his ability to get things done efficiently and quickly, Judge Rouleau appointed him deputy clerk of the court for the Edmonton judicial division, a position he was to hold until his death in 1916.

Taylor and his wife celebrated the birth of their first child, a daughter Eleanor, shortly after their new house on Fourth Street was completed. It was built just across the road from the Presbyterian Church, of which Taylor was an active member and respected elder.

Mrs. Taylor was also an active member of the community, taking a leading role in town and church projects. She had an interest in gardening and must have possessed quite a green thumb, as she won many prizes for her entries in the village's agricultural exhibitions.

During the summer, Taylor worked to expand his telephone system. On November 13, 1886, the paper reported that two telephones manufactured by the Molecular Telephone Company of New York were hooked up between the Hudson's Bay Company office and the Chief Factor's residence.

There is some question about the locations of the third and fourth phones in Taylor's system, but if the paper's story is accurate, then the second telephone line in Taylor's sytem would have run from the telegraph office to the Hudson's Bay Fort, with an extension line running from the Fort office to the Hardisty house, located up the hill north of the Fort.

On the other hand, if the paper's story is inaccurate, then the tale told by Taylor a number of years later can be accepted. That is, that the second line connected one phone at the telegraph office to the phone in the Hudson's Bay office. This would mean that Taylor had two phones in his telegraph office, one at the end of the second or Hudson's Bay line, and one at the end of the first or the St. Albert line. (According to telephone personnel today, it would be safe to assume that Taylor had two phones in his office.) According to a report in the same paper a year later, there was no phone in the Hardisty house. There seems to be no way to prove either story, but it is certain that the third phone in the system was located in the Hudson's Bay office.

After the success of the second line, nothing could hold Taylor back from expanding his telephone enterprise. On January 25, 1887, he wrote to the Bell Company in Montreal of his proposal to start a telephone system in Edmonton. He inquired about telephone equipment and secured some advice through an exchange of letters during the following months.

By the summer Taylor had succeeded in convincing four more people to accept the new apparatus in their establishments, and at the end of August Taylor ordered four Bell phones for a total cost of $125.72.

W. Curran was engaged to construct Edmonton's third telephone line. By October the poles were in place and on November 5 the four new subscribers — Norris and Carey, Matt McCauley, the Ross Brothers, and the postmaster — were informed that their telephones were on the way. According to the published building costs for 1888, the line cost $400. It was completed by mid-November.

On November 19, the *Bulletin* reported:

Telephones are now working in the following places: St. Albert, Hudson's Bay Office, Norris and Carey's, the post office, telegraph office, Ross Brothers and Matt McCauley's. They will shortly be extended to the Alberta Hotel, Hotel du Canada, A. MacDonald and Co.'s, Fraser's Mill and other points. At present the instruments are on two lines, but if a sufficient number of subscribers are obtained, an exchange system will be established.

Just before the completion of the third line, telephone history was again made when Alex Taylor made the first long-distance call in Alberta. This story has been told many times, but it bears repeating.

Judge Rouleau, who resided in Battleford, the capital of the North-West Territories at the time, was the owner of a telephone. Hugh Richardson, the telegraph operator at Battleford, had agreed to borrow Judge Rouleau's phone and hook it into the Battleford telegraph line. Taylor in turn would hook his phone into the telegraph line, and at an appointed time, have a long-distance phone conversation with Richardson. The time arranged was midnight November 1.

It was arranged that the other operators on the line were to disconnect their keys to give better clarity to the voice transmission. The story continues that one operator had forgotten about the call and had gone fishing (at midnight?) and didn't disconnect his key. Taylor and Richardson consequently had to yell in order to be heard over the static on the line.

Of the event, the *Bulletin* reported:

On Tuesday evening, A. Taylor, operator at Edmonton held a telephone conversation with the Battleford office, distance 300 miles. The words were heard so clearly that even the tone of voice could be distinguished.

The St. Albert phone had been moved to the new mission building. The rate between the two settlements was 15 cents for the first 10 words and one cent for each additional word. The telephone at the time was still used like a telegraph. The operators at either end wrote down the spoken message, and in turn delivered it or read it to the person who had been "called." This system of communicating didn't allow much privacy, but even if the civilian could be trusted to speak into the phone himself, the operator would still be listening in to count the words spoken, in order to levy the correct fee. But telephones in 1887 were not for privacy, they were for crowds.

The latest amusement in Edmonton was listening to music played over the phone — an activity in which the elite in Quebec and Ontario had participated some years before.

The list of telephone subscribers was slowly expanding. In April of '88, Lafferty and Smiths' bank got a telephone. By May, brand new telephone poles, which could accommodate five wires, dotted the streets of the village. Other subscribers who joined that year were Dr. Tofield, P. Daly and Company, and the mounted police. In the supplemental estimates for the year ending June 30, 1889, $650 was allocated for a telephone line to connect police headquarters to the Banff telephone exchange. A few months after the RNWM Police were hooked up, the Edmonton village police were also connected. Telephones proved very useful in preventing and solving crimes.

In the community it became fashionable to have a telephone. Progressive business establishments mentioned their telephone connections in local advertisements, and the installation of a phone in a residence was an indication of the occupants' elevated status. The first person to have a residential phone was Matt McCaulay, the foremost champion of the community. Even the southsiders wanted to be connected by phone. By July of '89, Robert McKernan requested telephone service. It was a distance of two miles to his farm on the southside, requiring a long wire to bridge the gap across the river.

Another request for a telephone came from John Walter, who lived directly across the river from the Fort. By the fall of '89, even the horses were only a neigh away from their owners, as McCaulay and Ibbotson's livery stable office secured telephone connections.

Just before the decade closed a local dispute made the citizens angry and indignant. Alex Taylor received a message from Judge Rouleau, saying that Taylor was to continue in the post of deputy clerk of the court, *only* until a clerk at Calgary could be appointed. Waves of protest were immediately sent to Judge Rouleau. Edmonton could not let the seat of the supreme court be permanently removed to Calgary. The campaign was on. If Calgary was to be the seat of the supreme court, then Edmonton wanted its own judicial district complete with a clerk and sheriff's offices. Petitions were circulated for the appointment of Matt McCaulay as sheriff and Alex Taylor as clerk of the proposed Edmonton judicial district. Because the block in legal trade was affecting businessmen, the Board of Trade also sent a resolution to the Minister of Justice.

The community action was successful, for Edmonton was awarded its own judicial district. Matt McCaulay was named sheriff, and on September 21 Taylor left for Calgary to be sworn in as Deputy Clerk of the Supreme Court of the Edmonton Judicial District.

Edmonton then turned its thoughts to the proposed expansion of its boundaries. The immigrants were coming and the citizens were getting ready for the onslaught. To the disenchanted in the United States, Europe and eastern Canada, the west was the land of freedom and opportunity, and the inhabitants of the land were ready to preach its attributes to all willing to listen. Many listened and were to come in the decade known as the Gay Nineties.

The Edmonton District Telephone Company

In 1890 Edmonton was a bustling community of five hundred people and numerous businesses which included six mercantile establishments — hardware, drug, jewellery, stationery, furniture and millinery stores — a newspaper office, and a shoe, harness and tailor shop. The town supported four blacksmiths, two carpenter and two butcher shops, a bakery, a boat building and carriage repairing establishment, a photograph gallery, four hotels, a large grist and saw mill, and a brickyard. Services included four churches, two schools, a Dominion lands agency, registry office, crown timber office, telegraph office, post office, police station and telephone system. The supreme court sat at Edmonton twice a year and the town had steamboat navigation on the Saskatchewan River. There were 5131 acres under cultivation, 3649 cattle, 953 horses, 1483 pigs and 707 sheep. Edmonton was rich in fertile soil, coal, timber and gold. It was the trade centre for the MacKenzie basin, and was the gateway to the vast resources of the north. Clearly, for any adventurous and fortune-seeking person, Edmonton was the place to settle down.

On July 21, 1890, there was a sod turning ceremony to mark the start of the Edmonton to Calgary railroad. There was talk of town incorporation. The newspaper office and Board of Trade members were busy opening mail from potential immigrants, and sending them eloquent replies on the glories of Edmonton.

By late summer, Taylor found that his varied business enterprises were short of cash. He decided to use his telephone system, consisting of sixteen Bell telephones and all the wires, brackets, insulators and poles, as collateral on a $250 loan. Taylor borrowed the money from his friend John Alexander Mitchell, who had been a part of Taylor's pre-*Bulletin* telegraphic news service in 1880 and was now a clerk in the Indian Affairs Department in Regina. As specified in the handwritten document, the loan was repaid within six months at eight percent interest. Taylor's faith was well placed, and as soon as he repaid his loan he proceeded to hook up the next subscriber to his telephone network. Donald Ross, of the Edmonton Hotel, finally got a telephone in his popular saloon, to the great joy of the suffering wives of many of his loyal customers.

Since the start of the construction on the Calgary to Edmonton railroad, a fierce battle had been waged between Strathcona, Edmonton, Clover Bar and Fort Saskatchewan as to where the new railway terminal should be located. The railway terminal would be a great asset in attracting business capital and new people. Competing opinions were loudly debated until at last the decision was made to locate in Strathcona. Taylor made an agreement with the railroad to put a telephone in the station, and as the last nail was pounded into the building, the owner and manager of the telephone company was there, wire and instrument in hand, ready to connect the station with the business section of Edmonton. This particular instrument, it was strongly stated, could be used only for business pertaining to the railroad.

The telephone business was not Taylor's only enterprise. For some time he had been working very hard on another of his dreams — that of constructing and operating an electric light system for Edmonton. In the fall, as the project was nearing completion, he promised the citizens that their village would be bathed in electric lights by Christmas. All Edmonton was aglow by the holiday season, but even electric lights couldn't brighten the Taylor household. Mrs. Taylor, the mother of Eleanor, James and one-year-old Walker, died suddenly on November 20. Harriet Taylor had been a highly respected member of the Presbyterian Church and the entire community. The high regard held for the Taylor family was clearly shown at her funeral, which was described as one of the largest in the history of the town.

By 1892, telephone business had increased to such an extent that in May the first switchboard, a second-hand Bell instrument worth $200, was installed. The previous month, Taylor had engaged a young man to work as engineer for his telephone and electric light plants.

Arthur William Ormsby, a native of Orillia, had worked with Bell equipment in the east and he quickly proved his competence. The second day he was in town he earned 50 cents for fixing the telephone in the *Bulletin* office. Arthur Ormsby soon showed his expertise in all aspects of telephony and electricity, and quickly became a respected member of the community. He was a far-sighted man and saw Edmonton's potential for growth. His faith in Edmonton's future was rewarded in later years when his real estate investments left him a wealthy man. His first house was on the spot where Edmonton Centre is today. It was a modest affair, just a three-room shack with a lean-to kitchen and a yard with a few farm animals. In 1912 he constructed a new house on 115 Street and 101 Avenue. He used ingenuity in building that grand house, for it was equipped with an intercom and heated by hot water.

Ormsby was one of the first members of the first volunteer fire department, and many years later he was made the city's first Honorary Fire Chief. He was also one of the founders of the Edmonton Curling Club. He loved to reminisce about how Matt McCaulay, Tommy Lauder, Alex Taylor and himself curled on the river ice in the winter of '92-'93. This was before a curling rink was built. It was mighty cold on that open air rink and got to be pretty dark at times. The foursome tried coal oil lanterns to illuminate the river, without much success, but they did manage to play about three games a week.

Ormsby himself was very efficient, and he expected things to be done immediately. If he was painting his house, he'd stay up until all hours to finish the job. He was a gardener, of sorts, and he placed the same expectations on his plants that he placed on himself. He bought all kinds of plants and literally "stuck" them in the ground. He seldom watered or weeded them, and if they didn't grow fast enough he'd pull them out. One year his daughter got him to plant raspberries but he pulled the plants out three months later because they didn't bear any fruit.

He was also an extremely friendly person. In later years Ormsby could be seen walking up and down Jasper Avenue, waiting to ensnare someone in a conversation. When his birthday rolled around, he would go up to the *Edmonton Journal* and have his picture put in the paper along with a little history. He died in 1961 at the age of 92.

While Taylor and Ormsby were installing the new switchboard, Taylor was looking for someone to operate it. Fourteen-year-old Janet Lauder applied for a part-time job. Jennie, as she was more affectionately known, was from a large family of six girls and three boys. James Lauder and family had moved to Edmonton in 1881, and in 1886 started Edmonton's first bakery and confectionery, which they owned until 1902. It was through Ormsby's association with operator Jennie Lauder that he met her sister and his future wife, Margaret Lauder.

Not content with the accepted pattern of young ladies, Jennie set out in search of adventure. School didn't thrill her at all so in 1893, when the school term was finished, she started working full time for the telephone company. She continued as telephone operator for a number of years, later became head operator and supervisor for the expanded company. In 1907 she left her job to marry William A. Griesbach, son of the famous Major Griesbach of RNWM Police fame. Willy Griesbach was a lawyer, and he opened an office in Edmonton. When the Boer war broke out, he enlisted and went to Africa. At the time he married Jennie, Willy was an alderman, and the following year became Mayor of Edmonton. He was a veteran of the First World War and gave the Griesbach Barracks its name.

Jennie's brother also worked for a telephone company. James Lauder was a first class electrician who worked on a long-distance line between St. Louis and St. Paul. In 1897 he moved to Laurie, B.C. to look after the telephone and electric light plant there.

Now Taylor had a switchboard, an electrician, an operator and a problem. The darn thing didn't work. It was discovered that the location was the snag to transmission, so the office was relocated at the rear of Raymer's jewellery store.

With confidence in the telephone system and its employees, Taylor turned to other pressing matters. On January 6, 1893, Taylor officially became postmaster of Edmonton. A few months later he resigned as telegraph operator, turning the position over to his relieving operator, George Voyer, originally of North Battleford.

Following Edmonton's incorporation as a town in the spring of '92, Taylor had been discussing franchises for his telephone and electric light companies with the town. In 1893 he applied to the government of the North-West Territories for official incorporation of the companies. Taylor had also decided to remarry, and in applying for incorporation named his intended as a shareholder and a director.

On May 27, 1893, the Edmonton Electrical Company Limited was granted a charter. The capital stock of $10,000 (1,000 shares at $10 apiece) was divided between the directors of the company — Alexander Taylor and Eleanor Sophia Marsh of Edmonton and James Mitchell Taylor of Ottawa.

On July 10, the Edmonton District Telephone Company Limited was granted a charter with a capital stock of $10,000. The directors of the company — Alexander Taylor, Eleanor Sophia Marsh, and James Mitchell Taylor — were incorporated "for the purpose of constructing, maintaining and operating works and apparatus for the purpose of operating a system of telephone and fire alarms, and any kindred system of electrical appliances, apparatus or machinery, the purchase and sale, leasing and renting of electrical appliances of all kinds and the carrying on of any other business usually or conveniently carried on in connection with any of the said systems, by the name of the Edmonton District Telephone Company."

Two days after official incorporation, Taylor signed an agreement with the town. Bylaw 52 gave the Edmonton District Telephone Company exclusive privilege of supplying electricity for the purpose of operating a system of telephones within the boundaries of the town for a period of ten years. There were a few conditions to this agreement. Taylor would keep the system in good working order, and would supply service to those who desired it. Places of business were to be charged no more than $36 a year and private homes $25 a year for services. Payments were to be made not more than quarterly in advance. Hours of the telephone exchange were to be 8 AM to 12 Noon, 1 PM to 6 PM and 7 to 8 PM all days except Sundays and holidays for the first year, and thereafter the exchange would run 24 hours a day except for Sundays when it would be open two hours during the day. One or more competent persons would be in charge of the office at all times. The company would also install a fire alarm system, and would use five fire alarm boxes to be erected at strategic points in the community. The fire alarm boxes were extremely important to the town, since at that particular time a pyromaniac was loose in the streets of Edmonton.

The next item on Taylor's agenda was a trip east. He left at the end of August amidst rumors of an upcoming marriage. While in Toronto, he attended the annual meeting of the Canadian Electrical Association and shopped for supplies for the Electrical and Telephone Companies. He then left for St. Thomas, Ontario, where he and Eleanor Marsh were married on September 25.

Upon returning from his combined business trip and honeymoon, he was faced with the problem of designing a suitable fire alarm system, a question which concerned many individuals in the town. In a letter to council dated December 6, Taylor suggested that the entire telephone system be utilized, "giving over 40 alarms, instead of only five as proposed." He went on to say that, "the telephone switchboard could be placed in the firehall, taking up about as much room as an ordinary office desk. The regular attendant would be on duty from 8 AM to 8 PM every day except Sundays, and for night duty, the alarm could be connected to the switchboard and in the event of an alarm being sent in, your attendant would be notified in the usual way. The great advantage, and it is the only one it possesses over the ordinary alarm, is that you have so many points from which an alarm can be given."

The fire alarm question dragged on and on and was never really settled to the town's satisfaction, but the five alarm box theory set out in Bylaw 52 did gain more proponents than Taylor's forty alarm theory, and the fire hall escaped becoming the home of telephone central. Perhaps it was felt that one Lauder at a time was all the excitement anyone could stand. The telephone operator was Jennie Lauder, and the Fire Chief at the time just happened to be a Lauder. Thomas G. Lauder, Jennie's older brother, was chief of the number one fire hall, and later was chief of the entire fire department in Edmonton. It was T. G. Lauder's son, also a fire chief of Edmonton, who presented A. Ormsby with his official Honorary Fire Chief hat and papers.

By 1897, the fire alarm system was still unsettled, but by that time ten phones were connected with the fire hall at night, and could be used for fire alerts.

In November of '84, telephone central again made a move, this time to the rear rooms over the post office. Construction began on two new telephone lines to the south side and the wires were hung the following spring. By the fall of '95, Taylor found that he required another full-time electrician to maintain the telephone system, as Ormsby was spending most of his time with the Electric Light Company.

Alfred E. Lee, a young Englishman making a tour of Canada, was hired. By September Lee was busy replacing the old poles on Jasper with taller ones which were built to accommodate a large number of wires. The poles made a vast improvement in the telephone service, as they would keep the wires free from all contact with electric light wires, business signs and other obstructions.

Alfred Lee was one of the telephone company's first "characters." He was born in England and came to Edmonton in 1894. A man of adventure, Lee never stayed long in one place, and when the Klondike gold rush began in '96 his wanderlust won out. He went to Dawson City via the Laird River Route and was the only member of the party to survive that trip. While in Dawson City, Lee found that prospecting for gold wasn't always as profitable as the newspaper accounts led one to believe. Lee wrote to Alex Taylor about conditions up north. Things had gone well for a while. He had a profitable contract cutting cord wood and was making a fantastic twelve dollars a day. In the first week he had an accident. He cut his foot, lost one toe and part of the next. Just before his accident he had accepted another offer to do some on work on the telephone system. Lee wryly told Taylor of his plight. He was sick in bed and his pantry was as bare as old mother Hubbard's. At this point a weaker man would have headed south, but Lee stayed and eventually built the first telephone system in Dawson City, Yukon. He loved the north so much, in fact, that he took his new bride, Elizabeth Calvert back after their June wedding in 1900. A son was born there in March 1901. Lee later worked as the Electrical Superintendant of the Dominion Bridge Company. He retired in 1948 and died in Victoria, B.C. in 1960.

By 1895, Taylor had made a name for himself as a sportsman. A golf and curling club had been formed and Taylor was one of the executives. His abilities knew no bounds, for he was an excellent curler and golfer. He won many medals and trophies, and probably discouraged many would-be contestants just by having his name entered in competition.

By this time telephones were entrenched in the lifestyle of the populace. There were over fifty phones in Edmonton and there were seven phones on the two lines to Strathcona.

One lovely day in the summer of '96, as the North West steamship chugged down the river, it broke the sagging telephone wires running to Strathcona. The damage was soon repaired.

Telephone lines were also being extended into the rural areas around Edmonton. In October, the telephone line from St. Albert to Morinville was in operation. The telephone central was located at the Missions in Morinville. For 20 cents a person could contact the central in St. Albert or Edmonton.

In the spring of '97 a tennis court was built beside Alex Taylor's home. Newspapers were full of talk about gold and the Klondike, the merits of various routes were discussed and Edmontonians touted their city as the gateway to that gold. Other subjects were mentioned occasionally, like creameries and railroad bridges, and the 112-pound pumpkin that Father Morin grew at the mission in St. Albert.

The telephone central got itchy keys again and in December of '98 took up residence on the top floor of the Gariepy block. Taylor experienced another tragedy when his second wife died. Shortly after, his mother arrived from the east to care for his household.

Immigrants, primarily Ukrainians or "Galicians" as they were called in those days, were flocking to Edmonton. Business was booming. These new citizens needed food, clothing and housing, and of course more telephones. In '98 a total of 2031 people settled in the district.

In March of '99, Edmonton's first pay phone was installed in MacKenzie's book store. For a paltry nickel the phone could be used for a call, regardless of the length of the call. That year 3209 people came to Edmonton, a telegraph line was built to Dawson City, the Boer War broke out, and Alex Taylor was elected president of the Old Timers' Association.

Longer Distance

Edmonton welcomed the new century with a sedate celebration. A watch night service was held in All Saints Church, and the cool air resounded with the ringing of church bells and with cannon blasts fired from the Hudson's Bay Fort.

Activity increased in April when a combined traffic and pedestrian bridge was built across the Saskatchewan River. This improved communications between Edmonton and Strathcona.

The telephone company was a definite success. Telephones had increased in number and popularity. The exchange remained open twenty-four hours a day, including Sundays. Art Ormsby, company electrician, had a busy summer installing telephone poles in St. Albert, and moving the telephone poles on the south side of Whyte Avenue to make room for a new twelve-foot sidewalk. Taylor put in a request to the Strathcona council for another telephone franchise in that town. He was also engaged in talks with the Edmonton town council concerning his tax notice. Taylor claimed that his telephone company evaluation had been $1000 too high.

By early 1901, the telephone company was sending tentacles further into the surrounding countryside. A telephone line was erected from Strathcona to Ellerslie and to Beaumont Mission. This line, connected with both Strathcona and Edmonton centrals, was built with funds obtained by selling subscriptions to the farmers in the Ellerslie and Beaumont settlements, and from donations by the Roman Catholic Mission and the government. The Edmonton District Telephone Company (EDTC) operated the line at a rate of 25 cents per message between Edmonton and Ellerslie and 35 cents between Edmonton and Beaumont. This fee covered the cost of maintenance. The phone at Ellerslie was located at the post office and the one at Beaumont was installed in the Roman Catholic Mission.

The telephone soon proved its usefulness in rural areas. A farmer could have instant communication with his closest neighbor three miles away or his friends in the city. In an emergency the rural telephone was indispensable. Even in town the phone was a great advantage in emergency situations. For example, the staff at the Edmonton Hospital could summon a policeman immediately if one of the inmates suddenly became insane, a situation that seemed to occur frequently.

The fathers at St. Albert had been quick to see the advantages of this new invention. They were willing to give the telephone a home in 1885 when it was rejected by Mr. McKenney. In February of 1901, Art Ormsby installed two small telephones and metallic circuits for private use and also a complete system of electric bells throughout the mission buildings.

The phone exchange became a permanent feature of Strathcona in 1901 when it was moved to rooms in the Rutherford block directly over the Gallagher-Hull butcher shop. Before that, the exchange had been only a part-time endeavor in the post office building. Miss Gertie Lynn was engaged on a full time basis to be in charge of the new telephone central. Strathcona's telephone service improved immediately, since the operator could devote all her time to the subscribers rather than divide her time between the telephone exchange and other business.

By December the demand for phones had grown to such an extent that the EDTC had to install a third switchboard at telephone central, giving a combined capacity of 200 lines. Three wires were now in use between Edmonton and Strathcona, and there were connections with St. Albert, Ellerslie, Beaumont and Morinville. St. Albert and Morinville had 10 phones, Strathcona had 25, and Edmonton boasted 102. To Torontonians, who boasted 8000 phones, the number would appear diminutive, but for Edmonton it represented prosperity.

With the new century came a new concept in business — civic owned and operated utilities. Neepawa, Manitoba owned its own telephone and electric light companies and was prospering. By the beginning of 1902, the Edmonton town council was seriously considering civic owned utilities, and the object of their immediate and serious consideration was another company that Taylor had started — the Electric Light Company.

At the same time that council was studying the implications of buying the utility company, the Bell Company was studying Alex Taylor's telephone company with what looked like the intention of either buying it or setting up direct competition to it. Since Bell was still unpopular with Edmontonians, this interest resulted in a swarm of stinging questions. If Bell bought out the company, the town could say goodbye to any idea of civic ownership. If Bell opened their own exchange in direct competition, small local businessmen, in this case Taylor, would be pushed out of business. The prospect of having to do business with Bell was not well regarded.

At the same time that council was beginning to see a Bell in every belfry, a communication from the east strengthened the opinion that Bell was a carnivorous beast waiting to gobble up unsuspecting private telephone companies. Council received a letter from Mayor Howland of Toronto asking the co-operation of the town in preventing the Bell Telephone Company from securing a monopoly and raising rates.

Bell, acting when it did, unwittingly added fuel to the anti-Bell feeling and served to prod council to acquire Taylor's Electric Light Company. The citizens of the town approved, and the Electric Light Company was purchased for slightly more than $13,000. Strathcona followed Edmonton's lead and purchased the electric light installations on the south side of the river.

In the meantime the rural telephone network continued to include more and more communities in its web. As soon as the frost permitted in the spring of '02, the telephone men put up poles for the new line to Leduc. The list of Edmonton subscribers kept growing until the three switchboards were up to their capacity of 200.

J. S. MacDonald, Superintendent of Government Telegraphs, made a trip west to see about establishing telephone connections between Edmonton and Stony Plain. That fall, he made another trip to the west from his headquarters in Qu'Appelle. This time it was to start construction on the telephone line to be built from St. Albert to Rivière Qui Barre by way of Rue.

By mid-September of '02, the Edmonton District Telephone Company's lines were extended from Beaumont to Leduc. The line was tested from Leduc to Morinville, a distance of fifty-two miles, and it worked satisfactorily. On opening day only one phone was hooked up in Leduc, with the intention that an exchange would be opened as soon as more instruments were procured.

Leduc's lone telephone was installed in the Douglas Company's building. The rate between Leduc and Edmonton was 25 cents, the same as that from Edmonton to Beaumont and Morinville. When the Leduc line opened, the telephone company announced its intention of extending service to Fort Saskatchewan. The line was to pass through the Clover Bar and Agricola settlements and have six toll phones on it as well as an exchange in Fort Saskatchewan.

In November, telephone gangs were rushing the work to completion before winter set in. A cleanup campaign was conducted in Edmonton. The poles that ran from Ross Brothers to the Hudson's Bay Store were too heavily loaded and were replaced with larger spruce poles. These poles, along with new poles for the electric light wires, were shipped by river. Also that month, the government sent W. McKay and a work party north to finish construction on the telephone line from Rivière Qui Barre to St. Albert. The poles were already distributed, and finishing work was going on at an increased pace in an effort to complete the line before the ground froze. Before that could be accomplished, J. S. MacDonald returned to arrange for the extension of the Rivière Qui Barre telephone line to the mission and farm buildings on the Alexander Indian Reserve, six miles to the northwest. When the line was completed in early January, phones were installed in the Gillis Store at Rue, at Potter's Store at Rivière Qui Barre, at the Alexander Mission, and at the government farm buildings on the Alexander Reserve.

In 1903, the Edmonton telephone service had been available 24 hours a day, 7 days a week for 2 years, but the Strathcona and St. Albert centrals were only open from 8 AM to 8 PM. This was fine for Edmontonians phoning each other, but no one could call out of or in to the town between 8 PM and 8 AM. This occasioned many complaints from Strathcona and St. Albert residents. There were 149 phones on the Edmonton exchange, 27 in Strathcona and nine in St. Albert. Although the subscribers weren't averse to having telephone bells ring at night, a set of bells which weren't welcome during the wee hours of the morning were cow bells. It seems that every cow in town was the owner of a loud set of bells, and the tinkle, tinkle the cows made while freely roaming the streets at night was keeping many citizens awake.

By 1903 the EDTC was prospering under the leadership of President and General Manager A. Taylor, Secretary George Jellett and Electrician R. D. Hunter. Hunter had replaced Art Ormsby when Ormsby joined the city staff as chief electrician after the city bought the Electric Light Company in 1902. Ormsby continued in that position until 1919 when he became a city commissioner. In 1921 he left the city to enter into private business.

In 1903 the company offered subscribers a choice of a phone book or a card index of telephone numbers which could be tacked to the wall beside the phone as a handy reference. Telephone costs rose that year when the company placed a tariff of 10 cents on all messages between Edmonton and St. Albert.

In 1903 Edmonton heard from the Bell Company. J. E. Bull, western district manager stationed in Calgary, spent one spring day in Edmonton talking with Alex Taylor about the telephone situation. The Bell Company was finally planning to build a long distance line from Edmonton to Calgary and down to Cardston. Bill intended to establish local exchanges in the towns along the route, and in addition, to build rural telephone lines to outlying districts east and west of the main line. Construction was to begin in the spring as soon as the frost was out of the ground. Bell wanted to hook up their long distance system to Taylor's Edmonton system.

Edmontonians had for some time been watching the movements of the Bell Company, and although it would be nice to have communication with Calgary, the long distance line was viewed as a threat to Taylor's system. The threat came from the Bell Company's agreement with the CPR. Where the railroad went, Bell followed, installing telephones in the stations. Was it possible that once Bell finished the long distance line, it would install a telephone system in the Strathcona railway station causing the system owned by Taylor to be cut off? Frank Oliver, Edmonton MP in Ottawa, was extremely vocal in his opposition to the Bell-CPR agreement. He saw an immediate and real danger in the agreement and was in favor of an amendment to the railway bill. The amendment, if passed, would compel the railway companies to permit the placing of telephones in their stations irrespective of any agreement such as that between the CPR and the Bell Company. If the agreement was still in effect when the Bell long distance line to Edmonton was completed, then the Edmonton system would be cut off from the railway station, which, in the words of Frank Oliver, was "the central point from which and to which the system worked." Oliver also feared that the other communities on the long distance line which had intentions of putting in their own municipal system, would be prevented from doing so. According to Oliver: "Where there are already municipal telephone companies, these companies will be forced out of business. The Bell Company will have gained a monopoly just as the CPR. And what happens when you have a monopoly is high rates and bad service." Parliament debated for some time on the amendment to the railway bill. By mid-July the government body decided to let the railway companies and the communities decide on terms for placing phones in the railway stations.

With the immediate threat of the Bell monopoly diminished, the telephone companies for the time being were out of danger, but development of the long distance line continued to be watched. Bell was installing its most up-to-date equipment on the line. The *Albertan* talked about a marvelous new invention to be hooked into the system. The calculagraph, or automatic clock used for timing conversations, was so accurate that it calculated in fractions of seconds, thus enabling long distance users to tell exactly how long they had been talking. Another new telephone with a slot machine attachment was to be hooked into Bell's system. A phone with a cabinet and a triple slot machine was to be installed in the Alberta Hotel. It would be used for local connections until such time as the long distance line was finished, then it could be used to call south as far as Cardston and north as far as Edmonton.

By June, the telephone line to Fort Saskatchewan was making splendid progress, as was one of J. Lubbock's teams in creating havoc on Edmonton's main street: "Dashing down Jasper Avenue, they came in contact with a farmer's team and wagon. The buggy was smashed and left scattered on the road. The team finally became entangled around a telephone post in front of MacDonald's pharmacy and were caught."

Telephone poles were at one time thought of as a hazard to horses and their rigs, but by 1903 the telephone had gained such status that it was the horses and other movable objects that were considered hazardous to the telephone poles. Protection of the utility was even written into the town by-laws. One by-law stated that if a building was to be moved or construction was to be undertaken near poles, the persons concerned were to be notified. Work could then be accomplished without damage or interference to the utility systems. In one case a wire was pulled down by a contractor while moving one of the offices next to J. H. Morris' store, and Taylor wasn't tardy in sending a complaint in to the town clerk. The telephone poles in Edmonton had been replaced in '02, and the company had just finished installing taller and heavier poles in

Strathcona. It was imperative that the new poles, carrying an ever-increasing number of wires, be protected from all destructive forces.

By mid-summer the telephone company's franchise was up for renewal and the town council began to negotiate for terms of agreement. One item the council felt should be included in the agreement was a clause guaranteeing the town some form of protection against the Bell Company. Council wished to have first purchase rights if the present management wanted to sell out. Taylor wasn't happy about that idea. He questioned whether the town would want to purchase a system that wasn't strictly municipal. The EDTC was also in Strathcona, St. Albert, Ellerslie, Beaumont and Leduc, and the company leased other lines. Besides that, Taylor felt that if a clause was inserted giving Edmonton first option to buy, it would be almost impossible to interest any outside capital if he wished to expand. In an effort to dissuade the city from pursuing the matter, Taylor offered to give free telephone service to some town officials, and he agreed to operate, at no cost, the fire alarm system.

Taylor had raised valid points. Council hadn't thought of how it would (or even if it could) operate the rural lines. Since time was running out on the agreement, council voted to give Taylor another ten-year franchise. Because of Taylor's opposition, the demand of first option to buy the company was changed to first right to buy the company or buy stock in the company. In the meantime the council would look into whether or not the town would be allowed to run the telephone system. The city solicitor felt that the territorial government would not grant power to a town to operate a telephone system which extended to several points outside the municipality.

Shortly thereafter, the issue was reopened when the mayor (who had been absent from council during the negotiations) returned and convinced council members that the new agreement afforded the town no special protection. The mayor was totally in favor of the municipal system of telephones and had pointed out the success of Neepawa, Fort William and Port Arthur in that area. Finally, after four months of discussion, an agreement was reached between Taylor and the town. For protection against Bell, a clause was inserted authorizing, if deemed advisable, the construction of a municipal telephone system. While the franchise was being discussed, the Red Deer *Advocate* came up with an interesting bit of news which further upset the town fathers. According to the paper, the Bell Company was forcing its way into Red Deer amidst protests from its citizens.

Bell telephone officials then began asking various Edmonton businessmen to house the long distance central, but public opinion by this time was so high against Bell that business establishments weren't rushing to accept the offer. By October, Bell finally got one businessman to agree to house the long distance central. D. W. MacDonald gave the company some space in his drug store.

Near the end of the month, the Bell executives paid another visit to the manager of the Edmonton District Telephone Company. None other than C. F. Sise of Montreal, the assistant general manager of the company, and J. E. Bull, the western manager from Calgary, came to visit A. Taylor. It was a public relations visit according to Bell, to inform Mr. Taylor of the progress being made on the long distance line. The poles were on the trail all the way to Ponoka, and the wiring gangs were already working their way north from Calgary. As each segment between towns was completed, the town would get long distance connections. Bell was also establishing regular telephone systems in towns that were large enough to support them.

As M. L. Madsen and his crew of forty Bell wire men pushed closer to Edmonton during the Indian summer weather, the town grew progressively more nervous about Bell's intentions. The statement made by Mr. Sise that it would be "very improbable that Edmonton would have more than one telephone system," did nothing to quell the rising distrust. When the town received a communication from Bell giving notice of its intentions to place telephone poles on certain streets, council realized its fears. To prepare for the invasion the city solicitor made sure he knew the powers a municipality had over the operations of the Bell Telephone Company within its boundaries. The company, in erecting poles on a street, could not place them in such a position as to interfere with traffic; the wires could not be less than twenty-two feet from the ground; and the work must be done under the direction of a city official. Art Ormsby, quite familiar with telephony through his previous association with the EDTC, was instructed by council to direct the Bell Company where to lay poles for the long distance line.

As the EDTC was completing its installation of poles in Fort Saskatchewan, the Bell Company was completing its long distance line. It was opened December 22, just in time to make 1903 the first year in which long distance Christmas greetings could be telephoned in Alberta.

Hello City Telephones

By early 1904, telephone poles were so crowded with wires that the Edmonton District Telephone Company (EDTC) had to erect a fifty-wire telephone cable from the central office at McDougall Street west to Second Street. Not only were more people demanding more telephones, customers demanded a better quality of service. The Strathcona *Plaindealer* led the campaign for an improved telephone system. Strathcona residents insisted upon having a night phone service. According to the *Plaindealer*: "When a night service is being asked for, a better day service should also be sought. The telephone intercourse between Strathcona and Edmonton is now so extensive that the three wires which do service between the two centres are in almost constant use, and in nine cases out of ten, when parties call up either town they are informed that the wires are busy and have to wait until they are disengaged."

Not just Strathcona residents, but all subscribers to Taylor's constantly expanding telephone system were demanding an increased quality of service. Wires were overcrowded, and the congestion was interfering with service in all areas. It was definitely time for a change. Either a new and improved telephone system would have to be installed or the present system would have to undergo extensive repairs.

The Bell Company was building telephone lines all over the countryside, connecting community telephone services installed by Bell. Taylor knew that if he didn't improve services in the town, the citizens would look more favorably on Bell's proposals. Taylor had several options. He could sell out to Bell or to the town; he could work at his usual pace and find himself in direct competition to Bell or to the town; or he could improve his own system as much as possible. He chose the latter.

While Bell was installing a telephone service in Lacombe, George Stanton was installing telephones for the new Fort Saskatchewan exchange. Then the company strung two more wires across the river to Strathcona, which greatly improved service, and appeased the Strathcona *Plaindealer*. A few months later, continuous telephone service was established in Strathcona, putting the twin towns in touch twenty-four hours a day, seven days a week.

The government was also busy extending its phone lines. A government line was put in from Spruce Grove to Stony Plain, connecting Wiley's Store in the Grove to the Stony Plain Agency, which in turn was connected with the Edmonton exchange. W. McKay, the official government telephone representative for the area, arranged for a line to be built from Morinville to Legal, and from Morinville twelve miles north to St. Emile.

As spring approached, area residents watched the Bell company march into small communities and capture the telephone market. In Edmonton, the case for municipal ownership increased as Bell became more powerful. At the annual general meeting of the Edmonton Board of Trade held in March, the following resolution was passed:

> The town council to take into consideration the necessity of purchasing the present telephone (town) system, as it could be worked very economically in connection with the town's electric light service.

Many of the council members had been advocating municipal ownership for some time, and felt that with the support of the Board of Trade, it was the right time to press the issue. During the summer, talks were held among members of the board committee and council members. Negotiations later started between the EDTC and the town council.

On Monday, November 7, Edmonton became a city. On November 16, the first offer was tendered by the city for the purchase of Alex Taylor's phone company. The council felt that the sum of $15,000 was a fair price for a system that needed "extensive uplifting." This figure included the telephone plant, and all the equipment except those telephones which had been installed since October. On November 17, Taylor came back with a counter offer of $17,000. Council agreed to that price, subject to the endorsation of the agreement by the ratepayers. The city would take possession of the system on January 1, 1905, but in the meantime it would have benefit of all the contracts made by the company. The company would continue to install the necessary new instruments and would retain complete management of the system until January 1.

The city solicitor prepared a by-law for submission to the ratepayers to raise the sum of $27,000, which would include $17,000 for the initial purchase of the system and an additional $10,000 for the necessary repairs and extensions to the system. The citizens would have almost a month in which to make a decision for or against a municipal system.

Public opinion was heartily in favor of municipal ownership, but for the few who were undecided or adamant in their opposition, editorial after editorial advocating city ownership appeared in the *Bulletin*.

The articles were generous in their praise of the EDTC and its way of dealing with the telephone subscribers. There was little cause for complaint as the service had always been extended as rapidly as the requirements called for, and the rates were certainly reasonable. But in view of the city's phenomenal rate of growth, the present system would have to expand and in order to do that, additional capital would have to be secured.

EDTC could raise the necessary capital only by raising the rates or by borrowing money from outside sources. This would make telephone service very expensive, and would be a hardship to both the company and its customers. If Bell bought out Taylor, Bell would gain a monopoly and could raise rates without any guarantee to improve the service. The same situation would result if Bell bought stock in the EDTC. If Taylor rejected Bell, it would probably set up a system in direct competition to Taylor and ruin his business. The idea of Bell gaining a monopoly in Edmonton and Alberta was repugnant. The municipally owned telephone systems in other towns were doing quite well financially and there was no reason why Edmonton couldn't do as well, especially when the existing system was already a profitable enterprise. Telephones could be incorporated with water and power, the two other municipally owned utilities, and be run profitably.

There was one snag to municipal ownership. What would the city do about the parts of the system servicing rural and outlying areas? The system had grown tremendously in the space of two years.

There was a total of four exchanges on the system — Edmonton, St. Albert, Strathcona and Fort Saskatchewan. There were 289 subscribers in Edmonton, 60 in Strathcona, 16 in Fort Saskatchewan, 14 in St. Albert and 11 phones on scattered farms, bringing the total to 390. In the four exchanges there were 150 miles of wire and eight switchboards with a combined capacity of 425 phones. There were other lines owned or leased by the company. The company line through Beaumont to Leduc was 26 miles long. The line from Edmonton to Fort Saskatchewan was double wired and totaled 53 miles. One of these wires, the farmers' line containing seven phones in the Clover Bar district, was entirely owned by the government. The company had leased the government line from Edmonton to St. Albert and from St. Albert to Rivière Qui Barre, 25 miles in all. It also had an arrangement with the government to use the line to Stony Plain, a distance of 23 miles. The company had a working arrangement with the people's line from St. Albert to Legal. There were four phones in Morinville, one in Legal, and four at Rivière Qui Barre. The total number of subscribers outside Edmonton city limits was 110. There was 150 miles of wire in the four exchanges and 151 miles either owned, operated or leased outside the four exchanges.

The EDTC's yearly rates were $36 for a commercial phone, and $25 for a residential phone. A subscriber owning both types of phones paid $50, and reductions were obtained for two or more of either the commercial or residential phones. There was a tariff fixed at 10 cents for 10 miles with proportionate reductions for greater distances. If the system became municipal, the city would have to ensure a similar rate structure.

While Edmonton was trying to solve this dilemma, Strathcona residents began to wonder what they could expect if the city did take over the utility. The EDTC had an exclusive franchise in Strathcona until October of 1905. At that time, Strathcona could either install a system of its own or sell a franchise to another telephone company. Clearly, it would be to Edmonton's advantage to continue the Strathcona franchise. It would also be to Strathcona's advantage because as the *Plaindealer* said, if Edmonton took over the citizens would certainly receive the "same high quality service at the same fair price."

At this point, J. E. Bull of the Bell wished to make it perfectly clear that the Bell had never wished to enter into competition with the EDTC or with the city. Determined to show the company's good will, Bell offered — in the case that the city buy the utility — to place at the city's disposal the experience and ability of the Bell's engineering department for consultation and help in the event the city would want to standardize the system. Mr. Bull claimed that Bell's policy was to "protect its own vested interests, not to cut into a field already occupied."

The local newspaper was not to be fooled by the ever-ready promises of Bell. "The Bell stands ready", it stated, "to purchase or freeze out the local company if the city does not purchase, or in other words, if the majority of votes is not pooled for the by-law." The *Bulletin* had made its point. On December 19, 1904, the ratepayers of Edmonton ratified By-law 4, which proposed to purchase the system for $17,000 plus $10,000 for improvements to that system, by an overwhelming 661 for and 63 against.

The city took over its new utility at the beginning of the new year, and its first official act was to retain the employees of the EDTC. George Stanton stayed on as manager and Jennie Lauder as chief operator. Two of the operators, Margaret Harford and Pearl Grant, took advantage of the change in ownership to ask for a $10 raise in salary. Being of delicate constitution (as women were in those days), the job of being constantly pleasant and cheerful to often inconsiderate and downright rude subscribers was sometimes more than a person could bear. The city council agreed and recommended raises on the basis of a sliding scale according to the length of service. Not only Miss Harford and Miss Grant, but all city telephone employees received their first raise in April. Stanton got $75 a month and Jennie Lauder received $40. Operators Miss C. Thompson, Margaret Harford and Pearl Grant each received $30 per month; Miss Leonard, the St. Albert operator got $10; Miss Gertie Lynn, operator in Strathcona received $30; and H. M. Andrews, the Edmonton caretaker got $2.50 a month.

The city obtained another year's franchise in Strathcona, and continued to service all other EDTC areas until an alternate plan could be put into effect. Edmonton was opposed to continued servicing of the rural areas, but the alternative — that either the Bell or another telephone company set up a system — was more distasteful. Another solution would be for the communities themselves to set up their own municipal systems, with the rural areas being connected to the closest town. As this idea was studied, it became apparent that most of the smaller communities did not have the resources or skills needed to form their own systems.

Another idea was beginning to gain support. The territory would soon be made a province and the newly formed government might be persuaded to take over the telephone system in outlying areas. As this could be done only after the government came to power, a more immediate solution captured the imagination of the city councillors. Council should seek the co-operation of the surrounding communities in joint ownership of the telephone system. One community alone did not have enough money to provide needed additions or alterations to the phone system, but with the combined credit of the municipalities, the system could be improved as quickly as possible. Each municipality, being a shareholder in the company, would have a say in the management of that company.

After lengthy discussion, Alderman Boyle put forward the following motion:

1. That the Edmonton District Telephone Company be reorganized as a municipal telephone company including all municipal corporations north of Wetaskiwin in the new province of Alberta.

2. That application be made at the first session of the provincial legislature for incorporation of a limited company known as "Northern Alberta Municipal Telephone Company Limited." Shareholders would be Leduc, Strathcona, Edmonton, St. Albert, Morinville, Fort Saskatchewan and any other municipality wishing to become a shareholder.

3. The municipal company shall pay the initial cost of $17,000 plus additional charges for improvements.

4. Each municipal corporation would be a shareholder and would jointly guarantee debentures of the company.

5. Each municipal company would have representatives on the Board of Directors in proportion to the shares held.

6. Provision would be made for extending the system anywhere in the province.

Unfortunately the other communities weren't enthusiastic about the idea. The large centres, like Edmonton, would have the money, the shares, the representation, and therefore the say. The municipalities could not see the advantage in sinking their money into a project that they could not control. The previous system had worked much better and the only way to maintain the same quality of service would be for the provincial government to obtain ownership and control of the small municipal systems.

The new Province of Alberta celebrated inauguration day September 1, 1905 and almost before the new premier, Mr. Rutherford of Strathcona, could don the garments of office, the telephone proposal was placed on his front doorstep.

Provincial progress was a bit too slow for Edmonton and while council waited for a decision, it took steps to improve the telephone situation in Edmonton. There were frequent complaints of poor service. By October, the switchboard at telephone central was full. The commissioners were considering installing a cable that would handle 100 pairs of wires. This would lighten the extremely overtaxed telephone poles and prevent service interruption due to adverse weather conditions. The town council decided that Edmonton's system had to be revamped or changed, with or without a telephone agreement with the other municipalities. While the city upgraded its system it would continue to service all outside areas with the least amount of capital outlay.

In the beginning of 1906, the Province of Alberta acquired from the federal government all the telephone rights to areas within the province's domain. Then the city drew up a resolution to give to the legislature suggesting that the government take over long distance lines and operate them as a provincial enterprise. This plan would effectively push Bell out of the province.

When the province decided in favor of public ownership of telephones, the city gradually sold its interests in the other communities. But, just before that came about, Edmonton added another item to its list of anti-Calgary grievances. In the spring of 1906, Calgary hosted a meeting of Alberta municipalities in which the Alberta Municipal Union was formed. At this meeting, it was unanimously decided to campaign for public ownership of telephones. After Edmonton's campaign urging the same thing, it seemed terribly unfair that the Calgary mayor didn't even invite Edmonton to send representatives to the meeting. The Calgary mayor (equally miffed) claimed that he had issued an invitation but had received no reply.

In 1906, Edmonton renewed its franchise with Fort Saskatchewan to operate a telephone system in that town, but the citizens of the Fort were becoming very unhappy with telephone service. The town clerk of the Fort sent a letter to the mayor of Edmonton asking that rates be reduced from $24 to $15 for business phones and to $10 for residence phones. The town also wanted an extension of telephone service until 10 PM nightly. In return for the reduction, the town "would grant an extension of franchise for another three months." Mayor Griesbach explained that the city was compelled to pay a license fee of $50 plus taxes on the poles and wires. The service to Fort Saskatchewan in 1906 had resulted in a deficit of $372.15, or in other words the city lost $1 a day. The Fort citizens weren't convinced by the mayor and still refused to grant a franchise, whereupon Edmonton cut off the town's services on February 1, 1907. Before the telephone service could be reinstated, the Fort would have to remit its license fee and agree to the rates already in effect. Then a franchise would have to be arranged or the city would demand its investment returned. If these conditions weren't met, the Fort phone system would be removed entirely. Mayor McEvoy finally acquiesced and Edmonton received another year's franchise.

Two months after signing the agreement, the Alberta Government purchased the Fort Saskatchewan exchange for $1100 and took over the trunk lines and farmers' phones. The government then offered the city $300 for the long distance line to Leduc. The city sold because Bell had already established a very modern exchange consisting of 15 phones in Leduc.

Eventually, all telephone systems not within Edmonton's boundaries were taken over by the province or by rural co-operatives.

The Road to Automatic

By November of 1905, the city was ready to call an end to the cold war between itself and the Bell Company. The improvements to the phone system could be delayed no longer and the city, somewhat grudgingly, decided to accept Bell's previous offer to help. The overcrowding was partially alleviated when the Bell phone men put up more cable on Jasper Avenue and set up an additional switchboard. These improvements were to keep the system in running order until a new system could be installed.

F. C. Paterson, general manager of the Bell western branches, and J. E. Bull of Calgary paid many good will visits to Edmonton. The company made it quite clear that with the charter it held with the Dominion government, it could invade the city and put up poles wherever it wanted to, but that was not the policy of the company. All Bell wanted was to provide its customers with long distance connection with Edmonton. Bell would even be willing to sign an agreement to stay out of Edmonton if the city standardized its sytem and allowed the hookup. And, since Edmonton had already decided to put in a new system, Bell would submit a tender since the company was also in the business of supplying telephone equipment.

The city council wasn't about to jump into a sea of telephone equipment without first learning how to swim. Mayor MacKenzie had made a trip east to look into the systems under consideration, the manual and the automatic. Although he favored the automatic from what he had seen, he was quick to caution against too hasty a decision. It would be better, he said, to continue with the present equipment until both systems could be thoroughly examined and council could come to an agreement.

Edmonton was already familiar with the manual system, but it was hardly up to date, so both the latest manual and automatic systems would have to be studied in great detail. Letters were sent to fifty cities in North America that were equipped with automatic exchanges, asking for opinions on the system. Alderman May suggested that an independant telephone expert be engaged by the city to examine the systems and make recommendations to the council. This would provide additional input and facilitate a sound decision. Shortly after, R. S. Kelsch of Montreal was retained as consulting engineer for the reconstruction of the telephone system. He was also to study the manual and automatic system and make recommendations to the council.

Kelsch examined three systems — the central energy or common battery manual made by Bell, the Strowger automatic system made by the Automatic Electric Company of Chicago and the Lorimer automatic system made by the Canadian Machine Telephone Company of Toronto.

Kelsch felt the Lorimer exchange was superior to the Strowger since it occupied less than one-half the space, and instead of individual switches for each subscriber, the subscribers were banked together in units of one hundred. Instead of independent action by means of magnets in the Strowger, the Lorimer mechanisms were actuated by a main counter shaft, geared to individual shafts for each bank, the shafts driving the gears in proportion to the number of subscribers. The mechanism in the Lorimer system was perhaps one-tenth of that employed in the Strowger system. The Lorimer did take longer to made a connection, but that was a minor detail. Summing up the argument for the automatic, he stated that it was not as secret as it was made out to be and since the automatic system had not been sufficiently perfected, installation now would result in that system being obsolete in a few years. Another disqualifying feature of the automatic was the tremendous expense. His report concluded that an up-to-date central energy manual plant would be more advisable than the automatic. According to Kelsch, the Strowger plant would cost about $40 per line, the Lorimer plant would be $34 per line, and the Bell manual $27 per line.

This report was not enthusiastically welcomed in council, for the councilors and the commissioners had conducted their own investigations on the systems and had come to different conclusions. Back in January of the year, the mayor and a few aldermen examined the Bell system in Winnipeg and the Strowger system in Chicago. They also visited Grand Rapids, where both manual and automatic systems were in use, and received opinions on both of them. In that city, the manual system cost approximately $9.40 per phone per year, while the automatic cost about $4.60 per phone per year.

The city commissioners' investigation revealed that the total operating cost of the manual, requiring forty-three employees, would be $17,760, while the automatic would cost $8,120 and would require only fourteen employees to operate. The commissioners felt that the automatic was the system of the future and the manual would be outdated shortly.

City electrician Art Ormsby favored the automatic. He was familiar with automatics for he had seen one of the first automatic systems in Canada installed. Charles E. Taylor, electrician, favored the Lorimer automatic system. The mayor and alderman favored the automatic because it was secret, fast, accurate, economical and easy to add on to. After the automatic was chosen, it became a race between the Lorimer and the Strowger. The Lorimer was chosen for two reasons: it was more economical and it required less room than the Strowger.

An agreement between the city and the Canadian Machine Telephone Company was signed at the end of May and contained the following conditions:

1. The Company would make and sell to Edmonton, seven sections of the Lorimer switchboard, a central office plant required to operate the switchboard and 700 Lorimer subscriber instruments.

2. The Company would deliver the switchboard, plant and instruments and install the switchboard and plant in a suitable building. The delivery cost was to be paid by the Company.

3. The Company would ship the switchboard and plant within seven months of the date, provided Edmonton's lines and wires were completely finished. The Company would install the plant as soon as possible. For each week that work was delayed, owing to the default of the Company or its employees, the Company would pay $100 in damages to Edmonton.

4. The switchboard and plant would consist of seven sections of the Lorimer system, 700 subscriber instruments, one motor generator, two one-horsepower AC motors, one one-horsepower DC motor, one ringing generator for AC and one for DC, one storage battery, one wire chief's desk and one distributing rack and switchboard cable.

5. The city was to provide a suitable building for the plant, which was free from dampness and excess heat or cold, with all the necessary access to the building. The city would bring the

telephone wires inside the plant and would not remove the plant without consent of the Company. The system would be operated for the first four months by an expert foreman to be furnished by the Company.

Confident with the agreement, Edmonton then turned its attention to preparing a suitable building for the telephone plant and maintaining an adequate operation of the manual system in use.

The switchboard that Bell had installed in April was full and the list of people wanting phones was growing quickly. Overcrowded wires led to intermittent service, and lack of experienced phone personnel led to many complaints. The scarcity of "hello girls" was not surprising since the job was very demanding. Also, most female operaters only worked for a short time as they had to resign when they married.

Because of the public complaints, the city decided to hire consultants to study the city system for immediate changes which would improve the present system and keep it in good running order until such time as the Lorimer system was ready to take over. McMeen and Millar, telephone engineers and contractors in Chicago, were retained as consultants to study the city telephone system and to plan the construction of outside wiring and a new central building to house the Lorimer system.

Shortly after McMeen and Millar were hired, the by-law to raise $65,400, the amount needed to install the new telephone system, was passed by the ratepayers. The McMeen and Millar contract was the cause of a dispute between city engineer Kelly and the city commissioners. Kelly charged that Millar wasn't an expert in telephone matters, expecially in Edmonton. Kelly said that he should have been allowed to go to Chicago himself to get expert advice and to arrange for the purchase of material. There would have been less expense involved and the work would have been accomplished faster.

In spite of Kelly's complaints, McMeen and Millar completed their report, at a cost to the city of $1200, and submitted their plans and specifications for the outside construction on the new telephone system. An earlier report on obtaining a more satisfactory service from the system in use contained the following recommendations:

1. That all Strathcona trunk lines and toll lines from neighboring towns be terminated before getting to central and placed on a separate switchboard.

2. That call circuits and order keys be provided between suburban switchboards and local switchboards enabling incoming calls to be placed direct to the operator, who could reach the line called locally.

3. That sensitive breast transmitters and order circuit buttons be installed immediately to enable orders to be placed by phone instead of being verbally shouted across the room.

By the end of August, city engineer Kelly was saying "I told you so" to commissioners and councillors alike, as plans for the new building and outside systems still hadn't been received from McMeen and Millar. To compound problems, irate citizens were loudly complaining about their inability to obtain a phone. Accusations were flying about that a person had to have friends in high places before he could get a phone. Finally, plans were received in September and turned over to city architect Magoon for elaboration so that tenders could be called. The consultants estimated that the new system would cost $49,625. This included the building and cable entrance, conduit system, underground and aerial cables, plus the distribution and substation wiring and protection.

In October, an historic event occurred in Edmonton. The telephone operators went on strike! Although the strike was only twenty minutes long, it completely tied up the system and left the entire city "off the hook", as the city government was unprepared for the emergency. There had been great discontent over salary and working conditions, especially in the recent months when the exchange was overcrowded. On October 9, a letter was published by the phone workers setting forth their demands. The ten switchboard operators had been getting $25 to $35 a month and were demanding a minimum of $40. The letter addressed to the commissioners was to be answered by noon, October 10. When no answer was received by 2 PM, the operators walked out. The office was deserted except for one lineman who held the board and answered subscribers with "nothin' doin'," or "strike on." The operators marched to the city offices and presented their case to Mr. Pace, the lone commissioner on duty. Mr. Pace, cornered, promised to recommend a raise if the operators would go back to work. Both parties agreed, and the telephone operators got their raises.

The southsiders were having their share of telephone troubles. Since Edmonton was going automatic, Strathcona was faced with changing its system, which would mean either installing a system similar to Edmonton's, or renovating the present system to be compatible with the automatic to be installed in Edmonton. After some study Strathcona officials came up with a number of alternatives.

One possibility would be to place the municipal system on metallic circuits with new switchboards so it could be connected with the Edmonton automatic by manual as long distance at the central office. Another course would be to install a new system similar to the present one. A third possibility would be to install an automatic system similar to the Edmonton system with a central office, at a proportionately high cost. The last alternative would be to give Edmonton the phone franchise and allow it to extend the new system to the south side. When all the alternatives were studied the consensus favored the last proposal. If the present system was kept, it would have to be metallic circuited. Installing a similar system along the lines of the present one would also involve a huge cash outlay. The idea of a new automatic exchange was certainly attractive, but $30,000 was a bit steep for Strathcona. Giving Edmonton the franchise would result in an automatic system for Strathcona, and the only cost to the southsiders would be the regular monthly telephone rental. The decision was made to extend the franchise.

At the start of negotiations, Edmonton asked for a 20-year franchise, in return for which the city would install an automatic central in Strathcona and string a 350-line cable across the river. More lines would be added when the need arose. At the time there were 250 phones in Strathcona and there were applications for 50 more. The cost of furnishing the town with insulated copper wire for the central energy automatic system, laying the cable and furnishing the instruments would be about $25,000. An agreement was finally reached at the end of December which gave Edmonton a 15-year franchise, and Strathcona an immediate connection with the Edmonton automatic switchboard by means of a 300-line cable.

Also by the end of December, it became apparent that the new system would not be installed that winter. Because of the early and severe winter weather, the contractors would not be able to fulfil their contract to have the phone central building ready by February. As it turned out, the delay would not complicate matters since the Lorimer plant was not ready to ship even though the Toronto company had sent repeated assurances that the plant would be ready to ship when the building was ready. By this time, the backlog of phone applications had risen to 130, and another 400 people had said they intended to apply.

It seems that Edmontonians weren't the only people clamoring for more phones. News at the start of January, 1907, was that lumbermen in British Columbia were working overtime trying to fill the ever-increasing demand for telegraph and telephone poles, and there was talk that all the 1907 orders couldn't be filled. The Alberta government had announced arrangements for construction of the first long link of its new telephone system. According to government spokesmen, the Edmonton-Lloydminster line would be one of the finest telephone lines ever built in Canada.

Another group working overtime trying to unsnarl the ever-increasing traffic tie-ups was the Edmonton city police. Everyone seemed to be in a hurry, especially the owners of those horseless carriages. The drivers thought they owned the road. According to one reporter: "During the rush hours of the afternoon, Jasper Avenue, the finest and broadest thoroughfare of the whole of the golden west, is frequently so crowded that a heedless farmer or truck man coming down the wrong side of the street will throw the whole stream of traffic into confusion and frequently cause runaways.

The police were forced to don their new fur hats, and stand out in the cold January weather keeping horses, automobiles and all other vehicles to the right hand side of the road. It was impossible to force the pace of traffic, which was exasperating for the auto driver stuck behind a slow horse.

The demand for telephones was so great that it wasn't long before enterprising people were engaged in the telephone blackmarket. With a population of 11,163 and only 650 phones in the system, the situation soon degenerated to a point where the city formulated and enforced a strict telephone policy. Subscribers could not sell their own phones, or rent, lend or remove them. If subscribers no longer wished to have the phone in their residence or place of business, they had to inform the city and then the city would send a workman to remove the phone. The city would then redistribute the phones. There would no longer be preference given to places of business or to professionals or prominent people, or people with relatives and friends in the telephone department. The city would distribute the phones strictly on a first come first served basis and there would be no exceptions. But still the allegations continued, and so did the blackmarket.

By the beginning of the year another commodity became scarce. Because of a shortage of bricks, the new telephone building was forced into concrete shoes and an ensemble of concrete blocks. Concrete was the only alternative to brick, as the building had to be fireproof and have the necessary strength to support the telephone equipment. This change of plans added another $3400 to the overall cost, and delayed the projected date of completion to March 1.

By February, the word "telephone" was becoming synonymous with "migraine." The new telephone system was months behind schedule and people were screaming for services. Bell wanted to erect poles in the city, a sure sign that the company wanted to set up a central in Edmonton. The new telephone system was going to cost about $100,000 and the franchise alone was up to $500,000. With that amount of money at stake the city was not going to let Bell win without a struggle. It would be a fearsome duel down to the last telephone pole. The commissioners informed Bell that the city would give the company connection with the automatic at the city limits before the Bell people could build in, and the letter advised Bull of the Bell to consider an arrangement on that basis. Apparently J. E. didn't care for the tone of voice used, for in retaliation, an article in the *Albertan* of February 8 quoted Mr. Bull as saying that "The Bell Telephone Company is contemplating an invasion of Edmonton. Whether we shall take such a step or not is a matter which has not been definitely decided upon. We do not know, but we are considering it very seriously."

The *Albertan* editors interpreted that statement to mean not only a declaration of war on Edmonton, but also a declaration of war on the provincial administration which was actively engaged in extending trunk lines and working in conjunction with the local lines owned by independent companies.

When the government accepted the position of public ownership, it promised low priced telephone service for everyone on the basis that the telephone was not a luxury to be afforded by the minority but a necessity that should be made available for all. The government would ensure a rural telephone service at a fair price. Bell, on the other hand, being in business for profit would not offer rural telephone service, or if it did the cost would be prohibitive. The telephone in rural areas was already indispensable. It was used as a rural news service. Teachers could use the telephone to teach during an outbreak of contagious disease or during storm conditions. One invalid mother had heard the marriage service of her daughter over the phone from a distant community. A lost dog had been recognized over the phone by his master when the dog barked. The phone was a lifesaver in time of emergencies. Legislation had already been enacted enabling citizens to own and operate their own system which would be connected by the government to long distance and trunk lines. It would benefit no one to get in competition with the financially powerful Bell.

While Edmonton was defending its front gates against the invading Bell forces, Strathcona was making merry in celebration. On March 15, Strathcona, with a population of 3000, became a city. Shortly after, the new city was awarded the site of Alberta's provincial university.

When the snows of winter had melted, a crack was discovered in the north side of Edmonton's new telephone building. The footings on that side would have to be replaced and Edmontonians could expect to wait a little longer for their new telephones. As if that weren't enough, another crack was discovered — this time in the Canadian Machine Telephone Company's story! The machinery wasn't ready. However, the city did nothing in protest because the building wasn't ready to receive any machinery. A few weeks later Edmonton learned that due to shipping delays, the Lorimer system that had been ordered more than a year previously wouldn't be installed in 1907. Edmonton and Strathcona were growing by 500 people a month, and if telephone applications grew in proportion, city hall would soon be buried under a sea of paper.

By August, Alderman Walker had heard his fill of Canadian Machine's empty promises. He gave notice of a motion to cancel the contract. Not only was he disgusted by Lorimer's erroneous reports, he was beginning to think that the Lorimer system was too experimental to warrant justification for the "interminable delays." If patriotism was the key to the council's resignation, there were at least a half dozen other Canadian companies which manufactured phone equipment. Alderman Anderson agreed with Walker, pointing out that only 275 Lorimer phones were in use in North America, all in Peterborough.

Mayor Griesbach reiterated that even if the plant was ready, the building to house it was not. Besides that, Edmonton was unfortunately not in a financial position to pay for the plant even if it had come in time. Superintendent Morrison of the telephones and waterworks department was also of the opinion that the Lorimer was too experimental. The phone was cumbersome to operate and easily put out of order. He was in favor of the Automatic Electric Company of Chicago with its Strowger system that had proven its effectiveness during the fifteen-year period that it had been in operation. Even the Bell Company's equipment would be better than the Lorimer plant. Again, Anderson, Walker, and Morrison were out-numbered and the city set in for the long, cold and quiet winter.

While Edmonton was sliding further behind schedule, the government of Alberta was busy hooking up towns on its long distance line. By the end of October Vegreville, Lamont, Chipman, Beaver Hills, Bruderheim and Mundare were hooked up, and connected with Edmonton.

By the middle of November, the telephone building was finally completed and the electricians moved to the new location, relieving some of the congestion at the city office. By the end of November most of the underground cable was in place. The city had been hampered in completing the projects by the cold wet summer. The weather conditions caused a large amount of the cable to become defective, and the concrete on the new building never got a chance to dry properly. The entire building had been damp and unfit to receive the machinery. In an effort to dry the building, the steam had been turned on in the fall.

When Canadian Machine was informed that the building was completed, the company wired that the machinery would be shipped by December. December came but the machinery did not. Another wire was sent, and in reply a long, windy, repetitive and vague letter was received. Canadian Machine Company was planning to ship in December but that "... of course is conditional upon nothing unforseen occurring... we should not be asked to send expensive machinery and expensive men to Edmonton unless conditions are such as will warrant the most speedy installation... Mr. Morrison wanted us to ship the exchange last June and later to satisfy the demand of the public and to practically allay the unjust criticism of our competitor, we did ship the power plant and storage battery, and I think that you will agree with us that the shipment was made at an earlier date than actual conditions warranted... " and on and on it went, but still Edmonton did nothing.

Then John McDougall was elected mayor by a landslide, partly due to his promise to do something about the deplorable state of affairs in the telephone department. One of McDougall's first acts was to send an ultimatum to the Canadian Machine Telephone Company. The balance of the equipment was to be shipped by February 1, and installed by March 15. If the company did not do it, the city would cancel the contract.

In another long, windy letter the company solicitors said that the city could not break the contract and engage the Automatic Electric people of Chicago because it would be a violation of the Lorimer patents, and if Edmonton cancelled Canadian Machine would sue.

Mayor McDougall was not easily scared and passed off the threat as a bluff. In the meantime, Charles E. Taylor, telephone expert, had been sent by the mayor to Toronto to see first-hand what the situation was. (It was mainly due to Taylor's advocacy of the Lorimer system in 1906 that the council decided to go with that system.) In Toronto, Taylor discovered that the plant would not be shipped for at least six weeks. Ten sections of the plant were ready and the other twenty were being assembled, but not one of the 1200 phones ordered was ready for shipment.

Taylor then went on to Chicago to look at the Strowger system. Taylor left Edmonton a Lorimer man and returned a Strowger man. The Strowger was far superior to the Lorimer because of the advances Strowger had made during the past two years. Strowger was now a central energy plant. The scheme of the branch lines were superior to that of the Lorimer. Taylor, being an optimist like his brother Alex, declared that some good had come out of the two-year delay. If Edmonton now went with Strowger, the city would be getting a much superior system to the Strowger of two years ago, and the Lorimer of today.

Possibly because of his excellent investigative work on the telephone situation, Taylor was later given another responsibility. He was appointed the superintendent of construction of the street railway and later was appointed superintendent of the system. He left the city employ in December of 1910 to become manager of the Tofield Coal Mines and was on hand when a major gas discovery was made in that town in 1912. He was also in Europe at the time of the sinking of the Titanic in April of 1912. Although fate saw to it that he wasn't booked on that fateful voyage, some of his papers regarding equipment he had shipped back for the Tofield Mine Company went down with the Titanic. He consequently experienced quite a delay in getting the shipment out of customs.

Just before Taylor's return to Edmonton, Mayor McDougall, Superintendent Cummings, and city engineer Kelly surreptitiously left town to check out the systems themselves. On February 4, council voted unanimously to cancel the Canadian Machine contract and engage the Automatic Electric Company of Chicago. Lorimer still sent feeble letters and at one point even tried to entice Edmonton into reconsidering by offering to supply a central plant for Strathcona. But it was too late. Edmonton wouldn't reconsider and Lorimer didn't sue.

John Wylie, the Canadian manager of Automatic Electric was waiting with a deal that Edmonton just couldn't refuse. The company offered to put up a bond of $25,000 and a $10,000 marked cheque to guarantee that the Strowger plant would be in successful operation by April 15. Wylie also pointed out that the telephone building could house equipment for 4050 Strowger phones, whereas it could accommodate only 3000 Lorimer phones. Chicago would charge $56,460 for 1200 telephones, the exchange, plant and freight and duty on the equipment. The company also agreed to reimburse the city for any losses sustained through lawsuits which could rise in connection with cancelling the Canadian Machine contract. The contract was signed February 25. Two days later the city began wiring for the new Strowger system.

While Edmonton was bargaining with Automatic Electric, Strathcona was trying to decide what to do. Would it be better to go with Edmonton if, and when, it got its new system? Or would it be safer to accept the provincial government's offer to install a manual? Obviously John Wylie was also offering the government a deal it just couldn't refuse, and on March 17, Strathcona accepted a new and improved offer. The government would install a Strowger automatic in Strathcona that would hook up with Edmonton's system.

By the end of March, city employees were busy unloading fifty huge cases of telephone equipment that had arrived from Chicago. Shortly after, all Lorimer equipment was packed up and shipped back to Toronto. By April 24, the first phones, mainly for business and professional services, were in use.

The new phones were described as "cussless, waitless, out-of-orderless, girlless telephones." Strowger was simply amazing. Fifty days after the agreement was signed, Edmonton was using its first Strowger phones. A private exchange would be installed in the temporary parliament buildings in the summer. The Strowger system being installed in Strathcona would have a capacity of 2000. The Automatic Electric Company was also furnishing long distance toll boards for farmers' lines, toll lines and pay stations around the city.

Edmonton's telephone system came of age on May 4, 1908 by joining 84 other North American centres with Strowger Automatic phone equipment. By June 30, all 1200 Strowger phones were in use and anxious citizens were awaiting 600 more of those marvelous dial phones.

The Wonderful Strowger

Although the Strowger was the talk of the town, not all voices were raised in praise. J. E. Wallridge, for instance, had some complaints about the new system — in fact he claimed compensation from the city! The $50 that the town offered Mr. Wallridge was considered compensation enough for the destruction of his property's aesthetic beauty when some of his lovely trees were removed and replaced by ugly telephone poles.

Some of the people also mourned the passing of one of the more human aspects of manual telephony, the "hello girl." No longer could the subscriber call up central and hear a cheery "Number please." In the Strowger system, the subscriber would dial a number, ring a bell and his call would be put through immediately. However it was in retrospect that the charm of the telephone operator was remembered, for just before the new system was installed the telephone operators were often criticised for being slow and inefficient. This was certainly unfair for it wasn't easy being a "hello girl." Each operator had a hundred or more lines to take care of. They were expected to answer calls immediately, which was difficult when a number of calls came in simultaneously.

People were often impolite and sometimes downright rude, yet the operator was expected to be courteous and cheerful at all times. To compound the problem of inconsiderate subscribers, the Bell manual that was in use was antiquated and subject to constant trouble. The noise in telephone central was deafening, since operators would have to shout directions to each other for calls to be connected to other boards. It was hard to be heard over the din of talking, shouting and ringing. With many an evening would come a raspy, hoarse voice.

The operators frequently had to deal with an ignorant public. For some reason, many people had the idea that the operator was an "information centre". One operator complained that a subscriber demanded to be put through to the party that he had phoned ten minutes before. How was she expected to remember one particular call out of dozens, she wailed. Bachelors would ring central and ask for cooking and household tips, and the occasional date; new mothers would ask about child care and men would come up with an assortment of questions, such as: How long does it take to go over Niagara Falls in a barrel? The six-hour day, consisting of two three-hour shifts, was almost more than the average young lady could bear. The majority of operators didn't stay too long in the business because of the pressures. Also, the policy of the city in forcing retirement on married women reduced the number of experienced operators available.

There weren't many men applying for the job. The reason women were given preference was because women were more suited to the job because of their "highly refined alertness and memory." Just before the Strowger was installed, there were fourteen female operators and one chief female operator earning $30 to $45 per month, and two male chief operators earning $45 and $50 per month. Even though a six-room cottage could be rented for $25 a month, or bought with the lot for $2000, the pay of the telephone operator was comparatively very low. When the automatic came in, many of the operators went out — victims of automation — but a few remained as trouble and information operators.

There had been other personnel changes in the telephone department. A. E. Morrison, who was superintendent in 1907 and had been relieved of the post for advocating the Strowger system, was appointed Superintendent of Government Telephones. He didn't remain in that position very long, for in January 1909, he left the government service to accept a lucrative position in Minneapolis. Cummings was appointed city phone superintendent after Morrison left, and remained in that position until April 1, 1909.

The Strowger system was highly praised. For the 1100 phones working, there were only three to eight trouble calls per day, which was less than one percent. In other manual or automatic systems in Canada the complaints were as high as eight percent per day.

Making long distance calls became easier. The Bell long distance line was transferred from McDonald's Drug Store to the new city telephone building and hooked into the city system. Now, instead of walking to the drug store to make a long distance call, subscribers could make the call with their office or residence phone.

Strathcona was making progress with its Strowger system. In May the government decided to build, at a cost of $6000, a two-storey stone building to house the new phone plant. The Automatic Electric Company was to supply the plant within thirty days. A few days after that announcement, the government changed its mind and said the new $10,000 telephone building would be made of brick.

In June, Edmonton sold the old Strathcona telephone system to the government. Although it was appraised at $1400, the city was lucky to get $1000 for it as the entire system would be useless once the Strowger was installed.

By the end of August, Strathcona had its new telephone system. Long distance central again made a move, this time from the city offices to the government telephone office in the Parliament building. A reminder of manual days disappeared when the old telephone poles along Jasper Avenue were taken out.

In November, an improved fire alarm system was incorporated into the automatic telephone network. To report a blaze, a citizen could dial "29", say "fire", and be instantly connected with the fire hall and the automatic desk. Once "29" was dialed, the caller was locked into the connection until the call was disengaged by the fire hall. This system would discourage pranksters and recognize false alarms, for the call could be traced to its point of origin. And if an excited person called in and neglected to give the address of the fire, the department would at least know what area the fire was in because of the trace.

By mid-November, there were 1250 phones in operation, 1500 including extensions. Of those, 360 had been installed since May. A number of long distance pay stations available to visitors and non-subscribers were located at the city phone office, the Alberta, Windsor, St. James, King Edward, Richelieu, Grand View and Queens Hotels, McKenzie's Book Store and the Alberta Livery Stables.

There had been 96 phones in Strathcona when the old system was abandoned and by November there were over 200, with applications coming in every day.

Edmontonians had good reason to be proud of their new automatic Strowger system. When J. McLim, prominent electrical engineer of Montreal, arrived in town, he too was duly impressed with what he saw. According to McLim, Edmonton had the finest electric light and telephone pole combination system between the Atlantic and the Pacific, and he should know since he had made a study of the electric light and telephone systems in all parts of Canada. The use of lanes instead of main thoroughfares for poles was particularly pleasing to the distinguished visitor.

A fortnight following McLim's visit, the telephone department had another reason to be proud. Superintendent Cummings was appointed a member of the American Institute of Electrical

Engineers, one of the leading bodies of electrical engineers in the world. Appointments were given in recognition of great ability in the field of electrical engineering. Cummings was the only person in Edmonton at the time who was a member of the AIEE.

In December two new 100-line switchboards were installed. Two hundred more lines were installed in February, and an additional three hundred were ordered in March. In April, 1909, W. R. Griffiths was appointed the new superintendent. He was greeted with a stack of phone applications that was to keep growing in size during the four years he held the position.

The business lines were taxed to capacity, a situation Omar Kirby and his crew tried to rectify by installing three hundred lines to the central office. In the meantime, Omar's fellow employee, John Wiley, was holding talks with the provincial government officials concerning the Strowger system for other Alberta centres. In June, the government signed an agreement making Calgary and Lethbridge, along with Edmonton, Strathcona, and Saskatoon, the only members of the exclusive Strowger club in western Canada. At approximately the same time, Saskatchewan, following the lead of Manitoba and Alberta, bought out the Bell system in the province.

In the political arena, a number of Strathcona citizens were campaigning for amalgamation with Edmonton, and a petition circulating in the town started the three-year campaign. In December, Edmonton's Mayor Lee was re-elected for the 1910 term.

On the city sidewalks, city physicians could be seen riding their bicycles. It was a bad example for other folk, and city police could no longer allow it. In the future, they said, all offenders would be prosecuted, including doctors.

At telephone central, Margaret Harford, a senior information operator, resigned after many years in the department. Ethel Lynn, a former city employee and government telephone information operator, took Miss Harford's place. Ethel was the younger sister of Strathcona's first telephone operator. It was on Strathcona's first switchboard that Ethel got her telephone experience. Many days after school was out, Ethel would go up to the telephone office and take charge of the board for a few minutes, giving her sister Gertie a well deserved break. Ethel often talked about the first call she answered. Instead of ringing up the party, she put the wrong plug in and gave a well known citizen "the greatest buzz in the ear he ever got."

On Boxing Day, 1909, Mayor Sherwood Herchmer of Fernie, British Columbia, phoned his buddy Willy Griesbach to wish him the best of the season. In doing so, he gained the distinction of placing the longest long distance call in western Canada, a distance of 700 miles. The government line through the Kootenay country had just been completed and the conversation was carried on without difficulty.

By 1910 the local police force was busy discussing ways in which the telephone system could be used to aid in the job of law enforcement. It was felt that the constable working the beat would benefit by having the use of a telephone. Since this was before the days of two-way communication in police cruisers (the only transportation at the time being horses) the logical place to put the telephone would be at a convenient and easily accessible outside location. Telephones were to be installed in boxes attached to telegraph poles. Access to the phones would be possible only for the foot patroller equipped with a key. Twenty signal boxes, one for each patrol, would be installed. A light would be placed on top of the appropriate poles, enabling a police officer to quickly spot the nearest phone location.

By April there were 1925 phones in use. At a rate of four installations per day, the 2000 lines would not last too long, and an additional 500 were ordered. By July, Edmonton had 2500 phone lines.

The Clover Bar steel bridge was completed and the first Grand Trunk Pacific train pulled into the CNR station. Work was progressing on the high level bridge. Edmonton entertained a distinguished visitor in the person of Lieutenant Baden-Powell, the founder of the Boy Scout and Girl Guide movement.

By August, the sterling silver reputation of the telephone system was beginning to tarnish. What was the department doing? Irate citizens demanded. A party of the first part could no longer talk to a party of the second part without being interrupted by a party of the third part or being completely cut off by some other party. The complaints came in at an increasing pace, and finally Superintendent Griffiths was instructed to submit a weekly "trouble and fix-it sheet" to help determine the extent and cause of the system's malfunctions. An urgent call was also put out for help.

P. H. Davenport, a Chicago telephone expert, was hired by the Automatic Electric Company to solve the problems. The company also offered the services of two of its experts. Initially, the department had decided to send chief switchman Lowry (later Superintendent Lowry) to Chicago to study the system in operation and construction, in order to have a trained Edmonton man available to deal with telephone disorders. The plan was postponed when the expected decrease in complaints only increased and the city accepted the standing offer of Automatic Electric to send its experts to Edmonton. The problem was somewhat alleviated but never really eradicated, since the population of the city and therefore the demand for phones grew at such a rate the department simply could not keep up. The result was a continuously congested system. By November, 2126 lines held 2406 phones on a capacity of 2500. Another 500 lines were ordered for installation in December.

Edmonton was looking forward to the 1911 telephone hookup with Spokane, Washington, and Superintendent Griffiths was looking forward with concern to 1912. He advised council to plan for a capital expenditure on properties for branch exchanges in Norwood and Groat Estates. The exchanges would have to be ready in 1912 because by that time telephone central would be overtaxed. The new residential areas would be better served with branch exchanges which would reduce the expense of long cable runs. By the summer, trouble calls were again on the increase, but this was due in part to increased construction activity which cut cables and hampered other outside telephone equipment.

Also increasing was support of the campaign for amalgamation of the twin cities. Committees were formed on both sides of the river to closely study the question of amalgamation. Cars were growing in numbers and an automobile club with 400 members was formed in the city. Edmontonians were proud when their dramatic club won the Earl Grey Dramatic Trophy at the Canadian competition in Winnipeg.

In Saskatchewan, the government was also increasing its ownership of telephones. It purchased the 700-line phone system in Saskatoon from the North Western Phone Company, who had operated it since 1906. The price tag was $70,000 for the plant, building and materials with the exception of the land.

The Alberta long distance and rural telephone exchange was moved from the Legislative Buildings to the telephone building on First Avenue North in Strathcona. In September the people of the twin cities voted for amalgamation and the government promised to turn its thoughts to the amalgamation bill at the first of the new year.

Near the end of 1911, the telephone department reported another surplus — $15,418 for the 1911 fiscal year, $4200 less than that of 1910.

Amalgamation and Expansion, 1912 to 1914

Early in 1912 city and provincial officials discussed the sale of the Strathcona phone system to Edmonton. The government was willing to sell, but only at the right price. Superintendent Griffiths and his foreman of construction made a cost survey of the Strathcona telephone system. They arrived at a figure of $75,000 for the plant, not including buildings, land and good will.

After months of delay, negotiations resumed in July and figures were bandied about. A price of $130,000 was set by the government at the beginning of the month and was raised another $20,000 by the end of the month. The city had decided to bid no higher than $120,000. Under the amalgamation agreement, which stated that the city had to supply telephones to persons within the city limits, Edmonton had to make an effort to purchase the south side plant. But if the government refused to lower the price, city officials would be forced to cancel negotiations. In order to keep its part of the bargain, Edmonton could build a system on the south side which would be in direct competition with the government system.

A cool war existed for about a month until the city re-evaluated the south side facilities and discovered that the government was not out of line in asking $150,000 for the system. When the government also agreed to transfer the private branch exchange in the legislative buildings the city agreed to a figure of $153,000. The government thought that that was a fair price for an exchange that would bring in a yearly revenue of approximately $17,200. At 7 AM September 9, the city took over the south side phone operation and the private branch exchange in the legislative buildings. At the time of the takeover, there were 673 paying subscribers, 18 complimentary phones, and 49 applications on file.

During the lull in negotiations, the government passed the amalgamation bill as promised, and February 1, 1912 was official amalgamation day. Strathcona hosted a greater - Edmonton carnival in the skating rink in celebration of the event.

By spring, the number of installations being done was at an all-time high, and Superintendent Griffiths was granted permission to buy a third horse and wagon. The system maintained a barn on Elizabeth Avenue to house the other two horse and buggy outfits belonging to the department. The heavy gang used the teams not just for phone installations, but for moving poles, conduit, cable reels and other equipment. Bicycles were used by the trouble shooters up until 1949. The departmental horse and buggy days ended in the 1920s, but for some years after that the department had an arrangement with the city stables to rent a horse and buggy in case they were needed to transport heavy loads. The outside plant forces became completely motorized by the 1940s, although several inspectors continued to work on foot or use the transit system until 1957.

At the beginning of May the department had a three-month backlog of orders. The 1000 lines added to the province's south side exchange helped allay the pressure there, but the north side was still besieged. The tension eased somewhat when tenders were called for the new substations to be located at Athabasca Avenue and Twenty-First Street and Pine Avenue and First Street.

Edmonton was alive with activity that spring, especially on May 14. A reliable rumor had circulated the day before, to say that the Hudson's Bay Company was going to offer for sale a number of lots on the Hudson's Bay Reserve. That morning 1500 people were lined up, ready to wait ten hours just to draw a ticket giving them a chance to buy a lot.

Edmonton's main streets were busy too. It was hardly safe to go for a leisurely stroll down one of the city's thoroughfares without witnessing or becoming part of an accident. Horses were particularly susceptible to close encounters with the new motorized vehicles. Superintendent Griffiths no doubt felt life and limb would be protected in the motorized type of transportation.

He probably had that in mind when he asked council for a car for the department. With the addition of the Strathcona exchange and the two new north side branch exchanges opening up in the near future, the telephone chief needed reliable transportation.

Soon after, Superintendent Griffiths went to council with another request. Because of the tremendous growth that had taken place within the department in the previous six months, Griffiths felt that an assistant superintendent should be appointed. He wanted a man with considerable experience in telephone engineering. The commissioners were in agreement and two months later the city hired V. H. Calhoun of Missoula, Montana. Calhoun brought to Edmonton fourteen years of experience with several of the large telephone companies in the United States. Because of his experience, Griffiths requested that Calhoun be given a wage identical to his own, $3000 a year.

By autumn, telephone construction on the new branch exchanges was running behind schedule and the contractors asked for an extension. New cables were laid on the south side, eliminating unnecessary poles. The Industrial Heights residents sent petitions around requesting phone service in their area.

Telephone central became more modern with a piece of new equipment. The new information desk (or number 9 desk as it was called) was welcomed wholeheartedly by the operators. On the old information desk, each operator had a certain number of lines and could only answer calls coming to her part of the desk. With that arrangement, one operator could be sitting idle while another could be swamped with calls. On the new desk, each operator had access to all lines, therefore calls were answered in the order they came in. The arrangement ensured better work distribution and better telephone service to customers. Another feature of the new desk was its almost unlimited capacity, compared to a capacity of 10,000 lines on the old desk. Two full-time operators manned the trouble and information desk, assisted by a third operator during peak hours. If necessary, the desk could be arranged to handle four operators. When the two branch exchanges were in operation, the desk was divided into "trouble" and "information."

Although service was improved tremendously, the department stressed that the efficient service was not an excuse to flood the desk with unnecessary calls. Subscribers then had the same bad habit that subscribers of today have, asking information for numbers already in the book. Another bad habit was reporting "trouble" when the only trouble turned out to be the subscribers' impatience rather than a mechanical problem. In August of the year, of the 4108 trouble calls reported, only 1932 were real "trouble" calls.

By the end of the 1912 fiscal year, the department showed a surplus of $5000. When one considered the costs of purchasing the new trouble desk, switchboard, two new branch exchanges fully equipped, a horse and buggy, an automobile, and several miles of aerial and underground cable, plus the costs of construction and installation, the surplus was almost unbelievable. The accumulated surplus of the department was about $36,000. During all this expansion, the telephone rates had remained remarkably low — $20 for residence and $30 for business phones. In 1912 the telephone system required 74 employees.

The new exchanges were finally completed by 1913, but a few snags soon appeared. Not only was it difficult to get connections through the two new exchanges, it was practically impossible to get a connection through central office. To complicate matters, many subscribers did not receive a new telephone book.

Mayor Short, eager to prove that his new administration could clean up city hall, and a lot of other places too, promised improvements and changes in the telephone department. Mayor Short was true to his word but his cleanup campaign, it was learned later, was done on the quiet.

The Mayor announced that one of his improvements would be to replace the three-wire system with the new two-wire system. In the three-wire system the third grounded wire extended from the local ground rod to the subscriber set. It was used to number pulse alternately on the vertical or positive and the rotary or negative side of the line which became polarized after a talking "answered" loop was established. Street cars and dampness due to poor insulation affected the third grounded wire and caused considerable inductive noise and cross talk on most long distance and local connections. The system was costly because of the maintenance required.

Nothing more was heard of the mayor's sweeping changes, including the installation of the two-wire system, until April when the minutes of the commissioners' meetings found themselves in the hands of a local journalist. Secretly, several investigations had been conducted on the situation in the telephone department. Investigation of the minutes revealed that a decision was made on February 12 to engage a C. L. Zahm to report on the system. The city officials were familiar with Zahm as he was the electrolysis expert who a few months before had been engaged to report on the electrical leakage in the city's electrical system. Zahm's rate was $25 per day plus expenses, from the date of leaving until he returned to Los Angeles. The Zahm item was inserted in the typewritten minutes in handwriting and initialled by the three commissioners. Mr. Zahm was in Edmonton three days and left as secretly as he had arrived.

Another handwritten item in the minutes of the March 1 meeting revealed that the services of Mr. Owens of the Automatic Electric Company and Mr. Brooke, an engineer from Columbus, Ohio, were secured to investigate the phone system and make recommendations for improvements. The cost of that investigation, divided equally between city and the department, was not to exceed $1500.

Another bit of information came to light just before Superintendent Griffiths took a two-month leave of absence. Without any warning, an announcement appeared in the city papers that F. T. Caldwell of Spokane was offered the position of superintendent of telephones. The announcement was vague as to whether this appointment was permanent or of two months' duration. Since Superintendent Griffiths had not been consulted with respect to the telephone inquiries or the appointment of his "successor," Griffiths naturally assumed that the appointment implied permanence, and he sent the city officials his resignation at the end of April. Later, some of the department's employees were reported to have said that the contents of the reports of Zahm, Owens and Brooke were worthless and unreliable as to the statements contained in them.

On May 1, F. T. Caldwell became the superintendent of the city telephone system. He retained the position of inspector of the Home Telephone Company of Spokane, a position which would require his presence only once a month in Spokane. Caldwell had been in Spokane for three years organizing that company's system.

In a press conference later in May, Mayor Short said he was confident that a great number of improvements would be made in the phone system by implementing the changes recommended by Zahm, Owens and Brooke. He also expressed great confidence in the new chief of the department and anticipated a saving of up to one-half of the estimated expenditure contemplated for 1913, plus an increased and more efficient service.

Caldwell enthusiastically tackled his new job and during his first month of employment worked fourteen-hour days, investigating the system and making a report on his recommendations for changes. His first objective was to put the system "back on the trail and build a solid basis for the department." The new chief believed that under his guidance, not only would the department catch up with the demand for phones, but would be able to solicit new business. Advertising a city-owned utility was something hitherto unheard of in Edmonton. Caldwell announced that within three months three hundred more pay phones would be installed throughout the city.

Mr. Wylie of the Automatic Electric Company actively pursued Caldwell, outlining the benefits which could be derived by changing to the two-wire system. He claimed the new system would result in better service and material reduction in the cost of maintenance and operation of the company.

Wylie proposed to supply 10,000 lines of switchboard equipment with 8000 telephones at a cost of $525,480. Once all that three-wire equipment was in use, the city would be given a credit for an additional 4000 lines of switchboard equipment and 4000 telephones, a total value of $221,560 in return for Edmonton's old three-wire equipment. The credit would only be given in equipment and only when the new construction had been used. If the city accepted his proposal there would be an additional expenditure of $100,000 for a new building to house the two-wire equipment.

After studying the reports of Zahm, Owens and Brooke and Wylie, Caldwell came to the conclusion that while the two-wire system would be cheaper to operate and maintain, he wasn't convinced a changeover was best at the time. Thus the two-wire changeover that Mayor Short said he would institute was tabled.

When the electric light department moved to its own residence, leaving the telephone department the exclusive use of the whole building, chief Caldwell introduced a new scheme. A public party would be held at the phone office once a week, in order to better acquaint people with the phone system, and thereby save time spent in checking trouble complaints.

In the 1913 year end fiscal statement the telephone department showed a marked increase in revenue. Phone installations were up, cable and outside extension work had increased, and more lines were being added to all three phone stations. Also at the end of the year, the telephone department was again honored. For his contribution to the advancement of electrical science, J. P. Lowry, the superintendent of equipment for the department, was elected a member of the American Institute of Electrical Engineers, an honor given to not more than a dozen Canadians at that time.

The War Years, 1914 to 1918

In early 1914 another petition was going around (petitions being extremely popular at this time in Edmonton's history). This one concerned the south side telephone office. In December of 1913, Superintendent Caldwell began implementing another of his schemes to make the telephone department more efficient. Caldwell was anxious to amalgamate the south side office with the central office, as he felt this action would greatly improve bookkeeping practices and cut down on costs. He had talked, he said, with a great many subscribers living on the south side who were initially wholeheartedly in favor of the scheme. Unfortunately for Caldwell, once he put his plan into action a cry of protest was heard from the south side. It seems that Caldwell talked to the wrong people, or to a minority, or a great number of south siders had changed their minds. They wanted the Strathcona office to remain open! Those cold January winds had a way of making even the most apathetic person ready to express his opinion and by the fifth day of the new year, 205 Strathcona residents had signed the circulating petition. For support, the petitioners referred to a clause contained in the Amalgamation Act of 1912 which stated that the residents of Strathcona could have offices located in their part of the city where they could pay their utility bills. Despite their strong case, and the petition, the office staff remained in the north side telephone exchange.

Caldwell next concentrated his efforts on improving the monetary position of his employees. At the time that Caldwell accepted the position of superintendent, he stated that one of his priorities would be to get a higher wage scale for his employees. He was quite familiar with the city's reputation before he moved to Edmonton and it was hardly complimentary. Residents south of the border credited Edmonton with paying its automatic telephone employees the lowest wages of any city on the entire continent!

What could city council do after being presented with that evidence? The best way to dispel such rumors was to eliminate their basis in fact by raising the wage scale. In 1913, Caldwell managed to get raises for some of his staff and at the beginning of 1914 was in the process of negotiating with the city for a $9.35 a month raise, retroactive to January 1, for his technical men. The city government agreed to this demand but would not budge from its decision to deny the rest of the office staff pay increases retroactive to the first of January. Those employees would have to wait until March 1 for their increases. Caldwell came out of negotiations relatively content with the progress he had made.

Caldwell had a lot of other ideas. When he came to Edmonton, he stated that he intended to give Edmonton the reputation of having the cheapest rates on the continent. In addition, he was confident that the telephone utility could double its business, or take care of 12,000 subscribers, without raising the rates. He also intended to have 300 telephone pay stations in use by the end of 1913.

Unfortunately, Caldwell forgot to take into consideration that as telephone superintendent he was responsible to the city council and commissioners. The city government, alas, sometimes needed a lot of convincing before it would willingly give out large sums of money. Since members of city government were not always familiar with the needs of the telephone system, the department was not always given what it requested. Council was also getting pleas for money from all other departments.

As of July 1, 1914, there were only 9850 telephones instead of the 12,000 that Caldwell had promised. Six months later there were only 8375 phones, a substantial decrease. A year after the installation of 300 pay phones was to have been completed, there were only 20 in use. One reason for the decrease in the number of phones was the outbreak of World War I in August. As men left for the battlefields in Europe, many war wives moved in with parents and relatives and no longer required a phone. The main reason, however, was that in 1913 Caldwell realized that the department was out of money, and recommended that rates be raised. Many customers felt they couldn't afford the phone at the increased rate, others felt the phone wasn't worth the cost, and some, in an effort to reduce their cost, changed from a business to a residential phone. The result was a decrease in the department's revenue.

At this point, internal disagreement between telephone executives became public and started a chain of events which would lead to an investigation of the department, and Caldwell's resignation.

V. H. Calhoun, then assistant superintendent, was displeased with departmental affairs and made it known to the phone chief and the city government. At the same time he suggested changes. The rates should be returned to their former level, which would result in an upswing of commercial phone installations and possibly a reconnection of many residential phones. Also citizens previously requesting a new phone might put their names back on the waiting list. The department could receive the same revenue for 10,000 phones as the system was getting with 8000 and the city would be doing what a municipally-owned enterprise should do — give good quality service to the greatest number of people for the lowest possible price.

Calhoun suggested another scheme designed to make instead of waste money. At this time, the department was installing quite a number of private branch exchanges. The Hudson's Bay Company, Swifts, Burns, Revillons, some hotels and most of the larger mercantile establishments had private exchanges installed. Unfortunately, no contract had been signed, therefore any of these establishments could demand to be disconnected and have their phone installations dismantled at any time. A private branch exchange of over 100 phones had been disconnected in August, and a substantial cost was incurred in dismantling the system. The equipment would then sit idle until such time as another customer came along requiring a 100-line exchange.

In December, the Royal George Hotel ordered 60 of the private branch exchange phones to be removed. Calhoun suggested that all installations of that sort be made with a contract covering a period of three years. Not only would establishments be more careful in what they ordered, they would also take more time in considering removal of their phone equipment.

At the time, the department was spending $5000 to install a private branch exchange of approximately 250 phones in the MacDonald Hotel. For such a large exchange, a five year contract would be in order.

Two other department procedures which Calhoun felt should be revised or ended were developing grossly underpopulated new areas of Edmonton, and keeping on hand a large supply of material which would not be used in the foreseeable future. Calhoun also criticized the government's policy of spending money on itself for services that weren't required. The private branch exchange installed in the city telephone office on McDougall Avenue in 1913, which required the services of a $50-a-month operator to handle 12 phones, should be removed. The automatic sub-station, located in the parliament buildings, that handled the service of both the new and old parliament buildings, should be removed as well.

Then Calhoun opened the beehive! He raised the subject which would be a matter of city and province dispute for over sixty years. Calhoun's suggestion, had it been implemented then, would have accounted for more revenue than any other single proposal by any other telephone employee in the department's history! City telephones didn't receive any revenue from the toll business originating in Edmonton and handled over Alberta Government Telephone (AGT) lines. With his extensive knowledge of the system in the United States, Calhoun was in a position to make the assumption that it was the only instance where a system participant didn't receive a portion of the toll revenue. He found the situation most unjust to the city.

He estimated that from the years of 1909 to 1914, 15 percent of the aggregate total of toll revenue received by the province would be $155,000 — a figure he felt was more than generously in favor of AGT. AGT also had 400 lines receiving the full services of city telephones and for which the city received no revenue. For these services, Calhoun felt that AGT should be paying $6 per phone per year. AGT also had the use of 80 cable pairs belonging to the city, but the city received only $10 a mile when a figure of $15 a mile was more in order.

After Calhoun had brought these criticisms into the public forum, city council initiated a complete investigation of the telephone system. The point receiving the most attention concerned the toll revenue. The city telephone department did get some payment for toll usage of its equipment in later years, but didn't get any payment from the Trans-Canada Telephone System for toll revenue sharing until 1977.

Early in 1915, Caldwell resigned as the superintendent of the telephone system. It was said at the time that Caldwell had a lucrative position to accept outside the city, but most people felt that Caldwell had resigned because of investigations into his actions. The city governing body tried to quell the rumor and said that Mr.

Caldwell had handled the system very capably. Caldwell's resignation came quite unexpectedly and council was caught without ideas on a replacement. In the interim Jack E. Lowry, the first of the "Irish brigade", was appointed acting superintendent.

Shortly after Lowry was given the temporary post, there was talk that the electric light and telephone departments would be amalgamated under the supervision of Art Ormsby. Lowry could see no justice in that and was determined to take over permanent reign of the department. He had a lot of ideas and a lot of energy but first he wanted some security.

He applied for the job and requested an answer be given by December 1. On Decemer 4, 1915, the commissioners appointed him official superintendent at a salary of $225 a month, which was less than superintendent Griffith's salary of three years before. That $225 a month was just a start however, with a promise of more "when he shows his mettle."

"Showing his mettle" was exactly what Lowry had in mind. Lowry, according to one fellow worker, was a tough and taciturn Irishman with blazing red hair. He was even known to neglect replying to a "good morning" from his workers, but would get quite upset if he was not addressed each morning with a cheery hello. He was born in Ireland and educated in Belfast and at London's Electrical Engineering Institute. He came to Canada in 1907 and started with the telephone department in Edmonton the same year. When Lowry arrived he had no knowledge of automatic systems, for the telephone system in Ireland was totally manual. Despite this handicap, he advanced in a few years to the post of superintendent of equipment, the position he had at the time he was made phone chief. It was during Lowry's tenure that the city system installed its first two-wire equipment.

Shortly after Lowry's inauguration, Alexander Taylor, founder of the telephone system in Edmonton, died at the age of 63.

Although in his later years Taylor was afflicted with a paralyzing disease, he maintained his position of clerk of the court and devoted much of his time to his agricultural enterprises. Taylor had been the first man in the area to raise sheep, and by 1913 had probably the best flock of Oxfords in the district. The government evidently thought so too, as Taylor's sheep became the foundation stock for the Vermilion farm. By 1914 he was a well respected stockman in western Canada. A writer for a well known agricultural journal at the time made the following statement after his visit to Taylor's Stock and Dairy farm:

Mr. Taylor is a pioneer stockman in the Edmonton district and his influence on the livestock of this section during the early days, before the rush of immigration and the coming of the packing houses and government aid to agriculture, cannot be measured in mere dollars and cents.

It would be even more impossible to put a monetary value on Taylor's contribution to Alberta, in particular to Edmonton. He started the first news circular and was co-founder of Alberta's first newspaper. He introduced the telephone to Alberta and started the city's system. He introduced electric lights to Edmonton; he was the force behind the establishment of hospitals in Edmonton; for over ten years he was the valued head of the public school board; he served the town as telegraph operator, postmaster and clerk of the court. He put his heart into everything he did and tried to do as much as he could, never looking for recognition and praise. He is without a doubt one of Edmonton's foremost historical citizens and one of the great pioneers of Alberta.

Although the years 1914 to 1918 had great sociological and economic impact, the telephone department was little touched by the times it was in. There was almost no increase in telephones during the war years, nor was there any new telephone construction. Some telephone employees joined the services in 1914 and 1915, and ranks were somewhat reduced. Instead of hiring replacements, the remaining employees took on the extra work load as their contribution to the war effort.

Jack Lowry, in an effort to keep morale high and the department in good shape during these years, started the foreman's fortnightly meetings near the end of 1916. The purpose of the meetings was to "promote the spirit of co-operation among the different branches of the department." Papers were prepared and read at these meetings by the various department heads, with the object of spreading knowledge between the different branches. Some of the topics discussed were ideal cable construction, the management and operation of automatic exchanges, the relation of the business office to the plant, and the theory and operation of the mercury arc rectifier. At the end of 1917, a small book was printed containing many of the papers which were discussed during the first year of the meetings. The gatherings lasted only about two years.

Another undertaking of the department during this time was the quarterly publication, "Telephone Topics." Cyril Wates was the first editor of the magazine — which was only fitting since Wates had come up with the idea and Wates was undoubtedly the most talented writer on the payroll.

The object of the magazine was to provide an official organ which was to become a "common meeting place for the ideas of the whole staff of the city of Edmonton telephone department." This magazine was published until about 1926, although the last date of its appearance is not certain. The publication became a library of facts as well as serving as a news sheet for the staff. It also became a medium for many a would-be writer of prose, poetry and plays.

In 1918 the magazine was sent to the telephone employees in uniform in Europe and Canada, and after the armistice to those that still had time left in the services. The publication was a great success with those far from home, if the correspondence from them is any indication.

The department was very close-knit at this time. It was still small and telephone employees enjoyed a spirit of camaraderie. At Christmas, members that were away from home would receive packages from their telephone family in Edmonton.

One of those who kept the home fires burning was George Stanton. He had been manager of the telephone company back in the days when Alex Taylor was the owner, and was the most senior employee. One of Stanton's jobs then had been to install the Fort Saskatchewan telephone system. Stanton didn't seem to mind that younger men with less telephone time rose above him on the organization ladder. He was the foreman of the installation gang and loved to tell the women in the office stories about the "good old days." He also loved to collect what some people would call junk, but George saw treasure in a great many things.

Carl Tomlinson stayed with the department during the war. He was a trouble-shooter working out of the old union hall. Carl is best remembered by some as the victim in "the tire affair." It seems that some of his fellow employees occasionally removed the air from his bicycle tires and replaced it with water. After the war Carl married a telephone operator and started his own electric company.

R. G. Vanderburg was also in the city during this time and was chief installer for a number of years.

Cyril Wates, one of the telephone company's most accomplished persons, started before the war and remained with the department until the forties.

Doug Duncan joined in 1918 and was foreman of the south side exchange for years before he moved into engineering.

Ernie Ward was another old-timer who remained with the department during the war years. He had been an installer during the horse and buggy days. One story Ernie loved to tell was about the time he and his assistant finished the day's work early and decided to kill some time by having a well-earned rest. They got to the vicinity of Ninety-fifth Street and Jasper Avenue, hooked their horse to a convenient billboard and stretched out on the grass. After a two-hour nap they awoke to find they were missing one horse. The animal, apparently preferring the company of his own kind to that of two idle installers, pulled the cord loose and sauntered all the way down Ninety-fifth Street back to the city barns. The fellows, foiled by the horse, received a reprimand.

As Lowry was prospering in Canada, he encouraged two of his friends, Robert Christie and George S. Kirkwood, to come to Edmonton. The men had worked together in Ireland for the telephone system, which was under the jurisdiction of the country's post office department. From 1915 when Lowry took over as superintendent until 1951 when Robert Christie retired from the post, the "Irish brigade" was in command.

One of the women working in the office during this time was Amelia Baxter, who started in 1912 and was later to be Mr. Christie's secretary. Her brother Bruce later became manager of AGT. Ethel Lynn, sister of Strathcona's first telephone operator, was still with the telephone department, and was the operator with the most experience in telephony. Elizabeth Campbell, for years chief of the compilation staff of the directory department, joined the staff near the end of the war. Mary Jane (Minnie) Tebbutt also started in 1918. In 1928 she came chief operator, a position she kept until her retirement in 1960. Miss Tebbutt had the distinction of being the first woman to be retired from the city telephone department.

Jim McCool started in 1910 and served the department for 44 years, 32 of them in the position of assistant superindendent. When Jim joined the department, he handled the first advertising in the telephone directory. In 1913 he became an accountant and two years later was commercial manager. He was appointed assistant superindendent when Christie became chief in 1921. In later years McCool was recognized as one of western Canada's veteran telephone officials. He was widely known in Canadian curling circles. He was an honorary secretary of the Northern Alberta Old Timers' Association for 25 years, and was secretary-treasurer of the Alberta Curling Association for 17 years.

McCool was a good boss, according to his employees. You had to work hard, but he turned his head when tomfoolery enlivened an otherwise dull day and often took part in the fun himself. A risqué little joke was often awaiting the ears of a modest maiden and it wasn't past Mac to pinch the occasionally unwary backside.

During the days when McCool was commercial manager, part of his duty was to supervise the office staff. In 1917 the office acquired a new and ultra-modern adding machine. McCool treated that adding machine like a baby. He had almost exclusive use of the machine, and if anyone else required its use he would reluctantly consent, then hover nearby watching the proceedings.

At this time the accounts were entered and updated on big ledger sheets which the clerks in the office had to balance at the end of the month. They invariably had problems with their addition, and since Mac kept everyone away from his pampered adding machine, the young office boy (who got teased because he wore knickers) was called in to help.

The whiz kid was Buster Brown, later to become superintendent of the system. Clarence E. Brown was fifteen years old when he started with city telephones. He was an office boy for three months, then, on his sixteenth birthday in January of 1918, he transferred to the plant section as an apprentice switchman. He received his journeyman papers five years later and kept going right on up until he sat in the super's chair in 1951. Wages weren't very good when Brown started. Every two weeks he would take home $13.95, and that was for a six, not a five, day work week.

One of Brown's first duties as office boy came during the flu epidemic in the winter of 1918. He was given the task of spraying disinfectant on the public telephones in an effort to reduce the spread of the contagion. As a precautionary measure the medical people were advising citizens to wear gauze masks, which at the end of the day would be black with the pollution in the air. Brown would present quite a sight wearing one of the black masks and carrying his formaldehyde pump. This duty of spraying the thirty public telephones in the city made Brown the subject of a poem written by Cyril Wates, which went as follows:

STINKODORUS

The shades of night were falling fast,
As up the office stairs there passed,
A youth in mask of cheese-cloth made,
Bearing a pump from which he sprayed,

FORMALDEHYDE!

Around him, whereso'ere he went,
Hovered a devastating scent,
And any deaf or sightless gink,
Might trace his footsteps by the stink,

FORMALDEHYDE!

He entered through the open door,
And sprayed on ceilings, walls and floor,
On booths, desks, telephones and stairs,
On filing cabinets and chairs,

FORMALDEHYDE!

"Spray not my phone!" the cost clerk said,
"Those fearful fumes will strike me dead."
The youth exhaled an odorous sigh,
And squirted in his weathered eye,

FORMALDEHYDE!

"O cease!" the switchboard maiden cried,
"It makes me feel quite ill inside!"
He only gave his pump a squeeze,
And squirted o'er the jacks and keys

FORMALDEHYDE!

Next morning, at the close of day,
Lifeless but beautiful (?) they lay.
What made these harmless people die!
A voice came floating from the sky:

FORMALDEHYDE!

The Undertaker said, said he,
"Oh, what a cinch this job will be!"
He gave a mercenary grin,
"They are already pickled in

FORMALDEHYDE!

When he wasn't spraying, Brown and his fellow telephone employees were doing their part to help the flu stricken citizens of the community. In many cases, entire families were ill in bed with the virus and had no one to tend to their needs. The homes would be cold and there would be no food. The employees of the department would supply families with firewood and get the fire going. They would also supply and sometimes prepare food until a member of the family was well enough to care for the others.

By spring of 1918, things started to improve. The flu, which had caused so many deaths, was finally over. Telephone installations were on the increase, and to keep up with the demand the dispatchers received a new desk.

That fall, the four-year war came to an end. November 11, 1918 was Armistice Day, and a gigantic parade was held in Edmonton to celebrate the end of "the war to end all wars." The telephone department participated in the celebrations with a cable truck decked out with battery-powered eight-inch gongs which pealed joyfully amidst the hubbub created by a group of noisy telephone people. The telephone operators carried automatic phones which were triumphantly waved over their heads. One of the telephone cars also participated in the parade — or tried to. It was immobile more often than not and required an employee beside it ready to give the crank a yank.

By the end of the 1918 fiscal year, the department boasted 600 more telephones and a net profit of $35,000. This was the same figure the department had had in each of 1913, 1914 and 1915 — only in those years it was a net loss! Good times were definitely back, paving the way for the Rootin' Tootin' Twenties.

The Rootin' Tootin' Twenties

The January 1919 edition of "Telephone Topics" was declared the victory magazine. Superlatives flowed from the pen of editor Wates. The Allies had won, and the brave boys that escaped Flander's Field climbed out of the trenches and made their way home. One by one they returned — some to their families and their jobs, others to an empty room, a place in the unemployment lines and the task of building a new life.

The fellows that had left the telephone department in 1914 and 1915 to enlist returned to their former jobs, and some war veterans came to the department for the first time in the year following the armistice.

Ben Davison was back, a little older and a lot greyer. He had started with telephones in 1912, enlisted in 1915 at the age of twenty, and a short while after arriving in Europe was captured by the Germans. For three years he was a prisoner of war, laboring first on a work farm and later in a steel mill. He had a rough time, but fared better than many of those who didn't possess his skills. Ben returned in 1918 and was to stay with the telephone department for another forty-two years before retiring in 1961 as chief switchman.

Marshall F. Browse also returned to telephones after the war. He had been overseas with the signal unit of the 49th Battalion. Marshall served the department for a number of years, first as cable splicer, then as cable supervisor.

Big James C. MacGregor had been overseas with the 138th Battalion. Jim had come from Scotland and had joined the department in 1912. Jim stayed for forty-five years and was a foreman at the time of his retirement in 1957. Most of Jim's telephone days were spent with the installation crew, or heavy gang as it was called then. He was a very active member of the Norwood Masonic Lodge.

George Kirkwood, Lowry's Irish friend, was another returning veteran. George had started with telephones in 1913. He had enlisted when the war started and was stationed for the duration of the war at army headquarters in Britain, serving as a "sapper" in the communications unit. Kirkwood remained with the department until the fifties and is well remembered as an experienced and competent telephone man.

Cliff Butterworth, a telephone man since 1913, returned from overseas. He was wounded in action, suffering shrapnel wounds to his hands. Butterworth was in charge of the test desk, and it was his duty to check numbers after a cable accident. Cliff was a conscientious fellow but quick to show his displeasure by vigorously stomping his feet. He could turn the charm off and on and would do so when dealing with irate customers. He would handle the situation and himself in a most exemplary manner, at least until the customer hung up the phone. He would then flick the switch, fling his headset a few feet, and shriek a blue streak.

One familiar face around the department during the war years was seen no more. Jackie, bull pup belonging to Jim Ranning, the cable foreman, died before the turn of '19 and his master moved on to AGT. The telephone office had been Jackie's territory and he had strutted around as if he were the superintendent.

Some new faces appeared in 1919. Tommy Rae had seen action at Ypres and the Somme. He was a machine gun sergeant with the Saskatchewan 16th Infantry, and was awarded the Distinguished Service Medal for his heroism at Cambrai, a position on the border between France and Belgium. Tommy singlehandedly aborted an enemy ambush and saved the life of a wounded officer.

Rae had been the head timekeeper with the city engineering department before the war, but there were no openings when he returned. He managed to get a job in November of '19 as a cable splicer's helper. It was a cold job, he remembered, especially that first one — putting a new cable in at Swifts. "I walked around that pole till I nearly wore a hole in the ground," he recalled. Later, when Christie became superintendent, Rae finally got enough courage to ask for an inside job as a switchman.

Jim Sandilands, also a veteran, joined the telephone department in October of 1918. He was the maintenance chief for the downtown area and a very good person to be around if one needed to be cheered up. It is said of him that he was so familiar with the back alleys and back doors in downtown Edmonton that he could make his way from the Legislative Buildings to Churchill Square in the pouring rain without getting wet.

The economy was on the upswing. People were moving into the city and all of them wanted phones. By 1919 the demand for telephones was rising so fast that plans were hurriedly made for a new exchange building. Construction started that year and the building was completed in 1921.

Early in the construction of the new main exchange, Robert Christie, maintenance superintendent, showed that he was not just the good friend of chief Lowry, but was made of the same "mettle." During one part of the building's construction in 1919, the power in the city was temporarily cut off, and the almost impossible task of keeping the phones operable fell into Christie's lap. At this time, the telephone system depended on water for its water-cooled engine, and the water system depended on the city power plant.

Christie came up with a novel solution to the problem. Two barrels were placed on the steel-work of the main exchange building under construction. Water was siphoned from the boiler of the telephone building to the barrels where it was cooled, then into the engine that was set up in the warehouse. A continuous cycle was established between the engine and the barrels. The only problem with this set-up was that the barrels had previously contained pickles, and the smell emanating from the barrels when the hot water was poured in was enough to knock the most seasoned ironworker off the steel. Fortunately, the power came back on before the workers expired.

While the city anxiously awaited the completion of the new plant, the increased telephone activity caused overloading. The west end and north side stations were strangling in a maze of telephone wires. It was hoped that once the central exchange was completed, 1000 lines would be made available immediately. Of that total, 700 lines would be switched over from the north and west end exchanges, and the remaining 300 lines would be given to new customers who were clamoring for phones.

Unfortunately, of the 300 new lines remaining at the main exchange, only 200 were available for new subscribers. After installation, it was learned that 100 lines could not be used because of difficulties in numbering. Two hundred phones would not last long and orders for more equipment were sent off before the 200 lines were assigned.

The entire populace was excited about the new telephone construction, and it wasn't just because many more citizens would be hooked into the system. What really captured the imagination was the type of telephone equipment that was being installed. After six years of discussion, the city was finally getting the latest two-wire automatic equipment from Automatic Electric in Chicago. It had taken representative Wiley six years, but he finally convinced Edmonton to go with the new equipment. The new two-wire was a great advance for Edmonton. It meant economy of maintenance to the city, and to the subscriber it meant a great reduction in telephone trouble. Perhaps now a person could have a decent phone conversation without being upstaged by hissing and buzzing. It was said that the maintenance on the new system was so minimal that if all of Edmonton was converted to two-wire, only half the present staff would be needed.

The chief mechanical advantage of the two-wire was that it would do away with the third grounded wire which was constantly subject to disruption by frozen water lines or by a wandering current from passing street cars. Advocates were praising the system so much that some people began to think that its efficiency would do away entirely with maintenance crews — not such good news for telephone employees.

A modern telephone instrument went with the new system. Both wall and desk phones were reduced in size; a smaller dial was positioned at the base of the instruments.

By the spring of 1921, installation was completed by a team of workers led by R. O'Connor of the Automatic Telephone Company of Chicago. Edmonton had again outdistanced many of her contemporaries by installing the latest telephone equipment.

There was a sigh of relief on grand opening day. Having those extra phones would spell the end, officials hoped, of one of the problems plaguing the department. When subscribers moved from the city, they often failed to inform the department of their departure, and the new owners of the house or renters of the apartment would take possession of the phone. The names were unchanged in the directory, the bills sent under the former name were paid by the new tenants, and the new people had a phone. But citizens who had been waiting a long time for a phone were not at all pleased to learn that their new neighbor in town only a month had a telephone, and they did not. Consequently, the office was constantly getting calls about favoritism, which although untrue, besmirched the reputation of the phone department. Unfortunately, this practise did not cease immediately, as people still failed to report their comings and goings.

A few long-term employees joined the department at the time of the introduction of the two-wire, and they almost managed to stay within the telephone halls as long as some of that equipment.

A. M. Eager joined in November 1919. Alf Want started in January of 1920 and Wilf Kinney that September. These three men were each to spend over forty years in the service of the telephone department. Another long-timer was Bob Evans, who also started in 1920.

Alf Want started as an apprentice switchman working nine hours a day, five days a week plus alternate Saturdays, for a wage of 30 to 35 cents an hour. He was also on call in case of telephone mishaps, with result that, while Want didn't get much free time, he learned the system inside and out. He found it particularly interesting to guage the ability of the system to carry loads and to predict a snarl before it tied up telephone lines. Want became inside plant engineer, then plant extension engineer, and was systems planning engineer at the time of his retirement in 1967. Some years after Want's arrival, it became common knowledge that if there was a question with an answer that was hard to find, Alf Want would be able to help.

Wilf Kinney was a big Frenchman named after Sir Wilfrid Laurier. Wilf started in the plant as a switchman, moved into the position of foreman of the Granite exchange in 1948, then foreman of the Garden exchange in 1950. He moved into engineering, first as assistant plant engineer, then plant engineer, and finally chief engineer. Kinney was tough but fair, and would back his employees to the limit. He was as strong as an ox and once, in anger, bent a golf club in half. Wilf was a great sports enthusiast and a good curler and golfer.

Al Eager started his telephone career as a laborer digging for manhole covers. He retired in the position of supervisor of installations. In '39 when he was a PBX man, he completely wired the new Bay and Eatons downtown stores. Eager enjoyed his forty odd years in the phone department, even the times he had to negotiate telephone poles. He didn't do too well once, he remembered. Unknown to him, the base of a pole he was perched atop was rotten, and when he cut a wire leading to the house, the weight of the arc lamp unbalanced the pole. It snapped and down they went, hitting with an impact that "jarred every tooth loose in my body," claimed Eager. Al had worked for AGT before city telephones. He was homesteading in those days and needed the extra cash to get him through three tough years. When AGT could find no room for him one year, he joined the City Telephone Department. Thankful just to have a job, he neglected to ask what his salary would be. A few days after he started, his wife asked him what his wage was. When he said he didn't know, she suggested it was time he found out. Al approached Lowry one day after work and was told, "50 cents an hour, how does that suit you." It was just fine, as $22 a week was a good wage for that time.

Bob Evans didn't stay quite as long as the previous three, but was with the telephone department during the time of the infamous Fred Belanger. Bob and Fred had quite different political ideas, and Belanger never missed an opportunity to say something derogatory to Evans. This invariably left Bob fuming. Bob had a couple of other pastimes besides arguing with Belanger — babying his beautiful Boston Fern and betting the horses with Jack Clark.

Jean Duncan started in 1922, joining a female force which included Amelia Baxter, Elizabeth Campbell, Mary Jane (Minnie) Tebbutt, chief operator Lillian Soley, Jess and Lil Garden, Meta Robinson and Babbs Burrell.

For years Jean and Elizabeth worked in the compilation section of the directory department. Directory time was always a bit hectic for the last two months before publication, and the girls worked overtime every night. Their twelve hour day started at 8:30 AM. In the early fifties the directories were published once every eight months, and in the latter part of the fifties once a year. It seemed that the girls would be working overtime half the year and the rest of the year putting in a full week and a few more hours until noon each Saturday. All was not bad. On Saturday mornings Mrs. Christie would come along with a bag of fresh cookies she had just bought next door at the National Bakery. Jean retired in 1968. retired in 1968.

A few more unforgettable characters joined the department during the twenties, most of them staying for a commendable length of time. Bert Ross started in 1924. He learned the trade from Ben Davison and was main exchange foreman for years. Bert was a descendant of Donald Ross, friend of A. Taylor and owner of the first hotel in Edmonton. Donald Ross was later part owner of the Ross Brothers hardware business. The Rossdale Flats and the Donald Ross School were named after him.

Jack Clark started in '26 and stayed with city telephones for over thirty years in the capacity of night man. In the early days being night man meant more than checking cat meows and the rustling of bushes outside a window. Jack would answer repair and information calls and would be ready to lend a hand at the test desk during midnight hours.

Jock Saddler and Alf Lewis both started in '28. Alf Lewis, a cable splicer, had the reputation with the department of being a fast worker. Jock Saddler had been a sniper in World War I, and to say that Jock was a fantastic shot would be an understatement. He was on the Bisely team at least three times. His skill came in mighty handy during duck season and he was famous for his catches.

J. L. Kilpatrick, Harry Thorn, Morris Flowers and Alex Hinchcliffe all started the year the market crashed, signalling the start of the Great Depression.

Alex Hinchcliffe was a cable splicer. He worked out of the north stores building on 112 Avenue. Regular as clockwork, each noon hour, Alex would walk home for his lunch of a bottle of beer and a sandwich. The fellows called him "Shorty" because of his diminutive size.

Morris Flowers could talk almost anyone under the table and had an enthusiasm which was catching. Morris had a favorite expression "esprit de corps" — and he believed the telephone department was a breeding ground for just that. Another favorite word was "chum." Morris called everyone chum. He was in the reserve army for years, was associated with the Alpine Club and did a great deal of work with the Emergency Measures Organization. With Morris one could never by too sure if he wasn't pulling one's leg. He started as an apprentice switchman and ended his telephone career as central office control and analysis supervisor.

Les Kilpatrick was macho, tough as nails, an old-school telephone man. He loved to get into scuffles, and the story is told of a situation which almost proved too much for him. One day he passed by a developing riot between a few army fellows and some zootsuiters. He was ready to get into the fray, armed with a tool from the telephone truck, when he was caught by the local constabulary and put into the Black Maria. In order to save his job, and the company's reputation, he made a desperate attempt to flee when he reached the police station. When the doors opened he took a giant leap, but instead of making good his daring escape, fell and broke one of his limbs. It is probable that the story that reached the ears of the telephone chief was slightly altered, for Les managed to keep his job.

Daniel Ewing also joined in 1928. A Scotsman, he served Canada in both world wars, in the second as an Alberta instructor for an Edmonton regiment.

Near the end of the twenties, Vivian (Junkin) Boulton, who was to spend more than forty years with the department, came from Fenelon Falls, Ontario to work as an operator. Vivian, who was very active in church functions, was chief operator at the time of her retirement.

All telephone departments grew during the twenties. In 1922 the rates were raised from $28 to $30 for residential phones, and from $54 to $60 per year for commercial phones. These rates were still among the lowest on the continent.

In 1923 there were 13,200 subscribers. During that year 2270 phones were installed and 2286 phones were removed. People were very mobile then and most removals were not rejections of the telephone but cases of people moving to a new apartment or home. Installations out-numbered removals so much that by 1925 plans were again made for another exchange. In 1926, work was started on a modern, fireproof exchange building on the south side.

Work on installations was started in August. The cost of the building was $33,000 and the equipment a whopping $129,760. By the end of November the south side waiting list was 150.

Fortunately, by 1926 the cost of the two-wire equipment had become more reasonable. The city paid $59 per line in 1926 as compared with $130 per line for the main exchange equipment in 1920. The building and equipment were financed out of department earnings which had accumulated in the depreciation reserve account. Telephone executives congratulated themselves on the existence of these funds as, they said, the city was able to provide modern telephone equipment without raising rates and without adding to the capital debt.

The south exchange was the second step in the city's gradual conversion to the two-wire system. With the installation and cutover of 2200 lines in January of 1927, all south side subscribers were changed to the new two-wire system and the updated instruments. The old three-wire equipment from the south side exchange was remodelled and installed in the north and west end exchanges.

The twenties were exciting times. The city was growing, the economy seemed to be on a never-ending upward swing, there were lots of jobs and wages were good. A gay and optimistic spirit pervaded society, and long-time telephone employees look back upon this decade as the proverbial "good old days." There was time for social activities and sporting events, philanthropic endeavours and good old-fashioned office shenanigans.

The Telephone Society with its motto of "Co-operation, Thrift and Sociability" was very active during the twenties. It was famous for staging dances once a month at the old MacDonald Hotel. "They were the best darn dances in the whole city, best moneymakers around," C. E. Brown recalled. Jean Duncan and Amelia Baxter were usually in charge of the festive decor, which meant spending many hours making delicate paper roses and decorating the ballroom. These dances were formal affairs and there were no alcoholic beverages allowed. Jim McCool made sure of that: he'd stand by the door and act as bouncer.

The proceeds of the dances would go to the society for its various projects. One was the annual Christmas party put on for the children of the telephone employees. The operators and office girls would spend the Sunday before the party at the exchange wrapping parcels and making decorations. Jim MacGregor was usually Santa Claus. He was a big man and he fit the suit so well that only his own children knew who was behind the beard and jolly laugh. The adults did the entertaining at these events with skits and musical selections while the children would open presents and munch on Christmas goodies.

In addition to the party, the society would adopt four or five disadvantaged families at Christmas and provide them with food, other essentials and presents.

The organization also donated the silver medal for the sight accompanying competition of the annual Alberta Music Festival.

During the summer months, the group would hold picnics, and once or twice a year would have a party at Cooking Lake. Bruce Baxtor, Amelia's brother, had a lovely log cottage at the lake and would lend it to his sister to host the summer parties. When Superintendent Lowry was in command, the staff would congregate at his house on 102 Avenue and 124 Street, roll up the rug and have a real Irish shindig.

During the winter, the employees had many skating parties at the various skating arenas around town, but the favorite spot was the big lake. Fred Rayner would always get there ahead of time to collect some firewood, and by the time the rest of the party arrived would have a pot of coffee bubbling over an open fire.

Sports were popular in the twenties. In the fall of 1921, a number of hockey greats throughout the city got together and formed a mercantile league. The City Firemen, CNR, P. Burns, Marshall Wells, and the town of Evansburg were in the league. The sharp shooters in the telephone hockey club were Carl Tomlinson, Wilf Kinney, Al Eager, Jack Rutherford, Harvey Grierson, Ben Davison, Buster Brown, Glen Cornes, Harry Fawns, and Fred Rayner (coach).

Everyone was encouraged to attend these hockey games and cheer for the team. There was a double-header played every Tuesday at 8 PM, and tickets could be purchased at the office or at the door, only four for $1.00. One young directory gal who happened to be dating a member of the Northwestern Utilities team one year found herself in a bit of a dilemma. Who should she cheer for, her boyfriend's team or her co-worker's team? She chose the former and got quite a razzing for being a traitor.

Curling was another popular winter sport. The city team in '21 consisted of the four J's — J. McCool, J. Armour, J. Lowry, and J. Maxwell — who won a number of games from their arch-enemy and formidable foe, the AGT rink. Through the years curling remained one of the more popular sports and became an annual test of supremacy for the two telephone outfits.

In the summer, lawn bowling and golf were the main participatory sports. Lawn bowling was very popular in the city at the time. Competitions would be held within the department and a team of its best bowlers would be sent to the city finals. Golf, usually reserved for men, would be summer's answer to curling in the competition between the city telephone guys and the duffers of AGT.

Another popular pastime during the twenties and thirties was mah jong parties. This game was so popular that at least one day per week, fifty-two weeks of the year, about thirty people would gather to play for prizes put up by suppliers of telephone equipment. The suppliers had quite a sense of humor when it came to selecting items for prizes. For his winnings one triumphant evening, Alf Want was presented with a "thunder mug," which was a baby's pot. Fortunately the Want children were at the age where the utensil could be utilized.

While sporting events were sold out in the rinks and on the links, the employees didn't neglect their inside sporting activities. The staff was small and tight-knit in the twenties, and the name of the game was fun — only during slack times of course.

Initiation of new employees was a part of the office foolery. Each new office boy had the same trick pulled on him. He would be given instructions to go to one of the branch exchanges and pick up an important parcel. The staff at the main exchange would make a call to the exchange in question and would warn the boys that a "live one" was on the way. The fellows at the branch exchange would fill a large sack full of bricks or rocks and give it to the poor fellow to lug back downtown. When he returned, panting like a spooked horse, he would have to open the parcel admidst loud guffaws from his fellow workers.

Sometimes the initiation rite backfired on the pranksters, as in the Morris Flowers case. When Morris started in 1929, the fellows sent him to the north exchange via streetcar with a huge box filled with bricks. Morris obligingly delivered because he thought he was taking the north side boys a box of "impulses" — a non-existent entity, though Flowers didn't know it. When Morris opened the box, revealing not "impulses" but bricks, he thought the joke was on the north boys and had such a good laugh that the co-conspirators were completely deflated.

A new boy in the repair room also had to undergo an initiation. He would have a receiver secured to his belt, mouthpiece up. The fellows would then bet him a quarter that he couldn't drop a dime off his chin into the receiver. Determined to show his dexterity and win a quarter at the same time, he concentrated on the trick, head in the air, getting into position for the drop. In the meantime, a prankster got a pitcher of water and poured it down the front of the fellow's pants, leaving the now wiser initiate to walk around like a gorilla until he dried.

The new and naive weren't the only victims. A few executives were also the brunt of jokes.

One of the plant department foremen, when asked a question, had the habit of lowering his head, putting his finger to his chin and pondering his answer for a few seconds. One day, instead of a lightbulb flashing on in his head in comic-strip fashion, a container exploded sprinkling his head with water. Some pranksters had put a paper cup full of water behind the light fixtures in the ceiling, then wired it to one of the desks. When the foreman was in the correct position a button on the desk was pressed, releasing the water. The foreman never did figure out where the water came from, especially since no leak in the ceiling could be found.

Sometimes jokes intended for one person backfired and befell some other innocent. Tony Turner, Buster Brown, Harry Fawns, Ben Davison, Tommy Rae and Jack Rutherford were all in the same workshop and were continually harassed by one serviceman. One day they decided that turnabout was fair play. Just before the serviceman was to come along, they set a lard pail full of water over the door, which they left slightly ajar. When the door opened and the water bomb dropped, it was Cyril Wates that came sputtering up off the floor. He took it all in fun.

April Fools was a special day at city telephones. Strange things happened. Tools would be found nailed to the floor, rubbers would be found nailed to the ceiling, and the quiet sneaking and creaking around gave everyone the jitters.

The favorite April Fools trick was to get hold of a dummy receiver with the cord removed, put Lepage's glue and very fine black oil on the receiver cap, then call someone to answer the phone. The victim would have the receiver stuck to his ear before he realized he had been marked, and would almost need an operation to remove it.

No self-respecting office could forget about the war between the sexes and at city telephones the women were victimized quite regularly. One of the favorite pranks was shooting elastics at a certain part of the female anatomy.

One young fellow gave the women no rest. Art Hardy was a lovable guy and it was pretty hard to stay mad at him. One of Art's favorite tricks was putting water in the women's wooden chairs while they were out during lunch hour. The "squish" heard as they sat down would bring groans of agony at the prospect of having to spend all afternoon in a wet skirt.

One day one of the women came to work sporting a new pair of lovely leather gloves. Seeing a good opportunity, Art took that part of the chicken which goes over the fence last and put it in her new glove. When the young lady found the disreputable thing in her glove, a no-holds-barred war ensued and Hardy barely escaped having his feathers permanently plucked.

Hardy never said die. One day he and Harris McLeod walked into the directory office, grabbed Lizzy Campbell, laid her on the table and said they were going to take her appendix out. The boys looked serious and the screams that came from Lizzy were loud enough to have brought squads of armed men running to her rescue.

The fellows had a bagful of tricks which generally made life miserable for the women. In the twenties the main exchange building was not air conditioned. During some hot summer days the women were extremely uncomfortable manning the phones for hours at a time. The boys tried many ways to get the office cooled down and one of their schemes, although it did nothing to combat the muggy office atmosphere, did give a bit of fun. Pans of cold water were put on a window ledge beside a doorway, then fans turned on in the hopes of sending some cool air into the room. All that was blown about were the women's skirts as they walked through the doorway. That place became the favorite lounging station for the fellows for a while.

Another prank pulled with regularity and a surprising degree of success was the fire trick. In the old south exchange the long distance operators were housed on the second floor. Instead of running up and down the stairs the girls would drop long distance information cards down a tube through the floor leading to a basket in the office below. The men, during slack times, would start a basket fire and send the smoke up through the tube. Then they would listen in delight as they heard the bang and crash of chairs and feet running across the planks. Thinking that the whole building was on fire, the operators were exiting as fast as possible.

Sometimes the women fought back. One time Bert Ross returned from shopping at noon and left his package where it could be hijacked. Two of the girls removed the contents of the package (underwear) and replaced it with stones. Bert discovered the switch after he got home - though it seems he didn't laugh at the joke.

Although the women were picked on, they were also protected. Women were not allowed to work past 11 PM. It was a rule that operators on duty at night had to be male operators. Edmonton was pretty spread out during this time and there were bushy uninhabited spaces between the different residential neighborhoods. As most of the women walked or took the street car to and from work, it was considered too dangerous to go home alone after 11 PM.

In 1921 Superintendent Lowry left the city telephone department to become the head of Manitoba Telephones, a post he held until he retired in 1947. In Manitoba, Lowry was also chairman of the province's telephone commission and he took an active part in the founding of a radio station in Winnipeg and one in Brandon. He died in Winnipeg in 1951.

Lowry was a popular superintendent. According to one employee, Lowry made all his workers feel important, treating each as an integral part of the human machine that kept the telephone department working efficiently.

He often brought visitors to the main exchange, showing off his department and asking employees to explain the finer workings of the machinery to his guests. Very often, Lowry would show up with some guests at the most unexpected time. This habit could have been embarrassing at times but Lowry had a tactful early warning system. He wore hard-heeled boots, and his footsteps could be heard echoing through the halls a few minutes before he appeared.

On the few occasions that Lowry caught his employees in an awkward position, he pretended not to notice a thing. One instance of this happened one hot summer day in the operators' room.

There was a rule in the telephone department that a man was to be on duty in charge of the exchange at all times. Under no circumstances was that man to leave. This rule, as many others, was occasionally broken. The reason this particular day was that the operators were nearly prostrate from the heat and required some refreshments. Alf Want, being the man in charge that day, gallantly went out for ice cream cones. When everyone was about half-way through their snack, they heard the familiar "stomp stomp" out in the hallway. The employees heaved their unfinished cones behind the switchboard and not a moment too soon, as immediately after Lowry walked in with two guests. The women just about swooned as Lowry walked up to them and looked behind the switchboard. Although it would have taken a blind man to miss the ice cream splattered all over the floor, Lowry remarked that all was well and left the dumbfounded workers to thankfully clean up the mess.

Lowry was replaced by Robert Christie, his friend from Ireland. Christie literally limped into office. He had fallen from a pole on Armistice Day the previous fall and had seriously injured his spine. The rest of the staff weren't doing that well either, as most were sick or just getting over serious bouts with illness.

Christie had been an apprentice in the National Telephone Company at Belfast when he was fifteen years old. He came to Canada and joined the telephone department in 1910. He took a course in automatic telephony in Chicago in 1911, and in 1915 was appointed chief of switchboard maintenance. Christie was to hold the position of superintendent for thirty years. During his time in the department, the number of phones owned by the utility grew from 2368 in 1910 to more than 38,000 in 1951.

It was during the twenties that Cyril Geoffrey Wates, resident genius of the telephone department, came to national prominence. 1924 was the year that Wates became chairman of the Edmonton section of the Alpine Club of Canada. It was also in that year, on July 14, that he became the first man to set foot on the summit of Mount Geikie, considered the most difficult rock peak in the Canadian Rockies.

Mountain climbing was Wates' first love. He originally came from Trinidad and spent some of his high school years at one of Harvard's associate colleges in the United States. He was brilliant enough to have attended any college in North America and could have succeeded in a number of different fields had he not felt limited because of his great handicap. He was quite deaf. He didn't pursue any secondary education but rather came to Canada, thinking his chances to succeed were greater here than in the United States. He chose Edmonton to be close to the mountains.

Wates was an electrical wizard and could have been superintendent of the city telephone system. However he refused the position, saying that his mountain climbing, his writing, his music and his inventions were too important to give up or set aside.

Wates could write music despite his deafness. He wrote the music and lyrics of many alpine songs. He directed St. Paul's Church Choir and in 1917 captured the small choir shield at the Alberta Music Festival. He lent his talented pen to the pages of "Telephone Topics" as its editor. There weren't many issues that escaped printing one of his delightful poems about life inside the department. He contributed prose and poetry to various North American publications and he wrote many skits which were performed by the staff at telephone society Christmas parties.

One of Wates' more famous productions was a comic operetta entitled, "The Telephone Girl and the Toff." In this enterprise Wates combined all his musical and literary talents and directed telephone employees Jess and Lil Garden, Meta Robinson and Babbs Burrell to academy award perfection.

The operetta began with an opening chorus singing, "When you're feeling blue and your wife is bad-tempered, just ring up the telephone girl and you'll feel much better."

Another show stopper was the "Superintendent's Song," which in part went as follows:

"My sense of my importance,
Till I attained perfection,
For throughout my life I have aspired,
To hold some great position.
And now at last I have acquired,
My heart's most dear ambition.
My star of merit as you see,
Is now in the ascendant,
For none can match the dignity,
Of a telephone Sup'rintendent."

Wates wrote serious works also. He wrote a book on bridge, one on mah jong and some technical booklets on telephony.

To help himself in day-to-day affairs, Wates built himself an elaborate hearing aid. He wore a waistcoat that had little pockets inside which contained batteries that powered the amplifier for his hearing aid. He had an off-on switch on a piece of strap hanging from a pocket. Unfortunately there wasn't a volume control. His hearing aid was so powerful that if a person talked too close to him he'd get a terrific ringing in his ears and would back away. His deafness sometimes came in very handy, especially considering the fact that Wates shared an office with chief Bob Christie.

Although Wates could have been accepted into Mensa he wouldn't have passed the test to join the best workers' club. He didn't like any sort of routine, and since he was usually caught up in his writing or his mountaineering, Wates' work at the office suffered. This didn't please Bob Christie who was not only a hard worker but quite a perfectionist. When Christie started into him, Wates simply turned off his hearing aid.

One of Cyril's inventions was an electronic clock which hung on the wall of the main exchange building for years and was used in the telephone department's time service. In the twenties a subscriber could call "960" any time of the day or night and get the correct time. The exchange had a direct line to the Astro-Physical Observatory in Ottawa, which would notify the department at the exact moment of noon every day. This was almost an unnecessary service as Wates' clock was usually right on the nose.

In the early forties, Wates was despondent because his health was too fragile for the rigors of mountain climbing. Alf Want, in an effort to cheer him up, suggested they take up star gazing. Astronomy had always been one of Wates' hobbies and he would watch the heavens with a portable telescope. When Cyril replied that the telescope he had wasn't powerful enough, Want suggested they build a telescope. That idea opened a new door for Wates and gave him the opportunity to again prove his exceptional ability.

A telescope kit was ordered. Want got some glass and grinding components and Wates built a machine for grinding the glass. When Wates finished his work, the two-ton telescope was so perfectly balanced that when a bent pin was placed on one end, the telescope would tip. Wates presented this telescope to the University of Alberta in 1943 and also helped plan the university observatory. That year Wates received the Chant Medal of the Royal Astronomical Society of Canada for "outstanding amateur contribution to astronomy in Canada."

Wates and Want were also photographic enthusiasts and made good use of the darkroom in old city hall. Wates would take rolls and rolls of pictures of his alpine adventures. On one trip, Wates lost a very expensive camera. Instead of buying another one he designed a camera, and he and Want set out to build it. They were unsuccessful, but Want still has some of the camera parts in his basement as proof that they tried.

One thing Wates was not particularly good at was driving a car. Like the absent-minded professor, it was probably because he had more important things on his mind. Everyone would scatter when they saw Wates erratically driving his Model T. They would even seek shelter in buildings if they detected a passenger's profile, for he would be concentrating on talking to his companion and paying no attention to where he was going. Brilliant, talented and bubbling with energy, Wates was definitely a character of the type that does not pass this way very often.

With all this fun and frolic in the telephone department it might seem that the work did itself. On the contrary, the first and foremost duty of the telephone person was to perform his or her job, twenty-five hours a day, eight days a week and fifty-three weeks of the year.

Repair crews were the unsung heroes of the department. During the twenties, the telephone equipment frequently broke down, as it was much less reliable than today's sophisticated machinery. With the three-wire, crews were constantly repairing telephone lines that were out because of the grounded wire that was affected by stray electrical currents, frozen water pipes, and the slightest hint of dampness. During some storms so many cables were rendered useless that entire exchanges were shut down. There were also numerous power failures, and the telephone department's emergency power couldn't keep the system operative for long.

Repairing and re-assembling a 200 or 400-pair cable sometimes meant working for thirty-six hours straight. If wires were fused, each of the 200 to 400 ends had to be unglued then re-matched with its mate, which was very painstaking work. During the summer it was bad enough, but in the winter cable had to be spliced with bare fingers. Repair crews were constantly on call and it was to the repairman's advantage to live near the telephone office.

The heroines of the department were the trouble and information operators. They always performed a bit harder than their job called for. The twenties operator was perhaps most often misused as a "time and wake-up service." Subscribers would ask the operator to call them back at a certain time to be awakened from a nap, meet a train, go duck hunting or take a cake from the oven. Having unusual demands was one of the hazards of the trade and most were taken in good spirits, for during this time the telephone operator had a respected reputation to uphold.

Before the advent of radio, the telephone was the medium used to communicate news that couldn't wait until the presses rolled. Supplying hockey scores and Commercial Grad game scores were two important services performed by the city telephones. The play-by-play man would broadcast down the wire to the exchange, and the operators there would relay the latest scores to a number of subscribers at one time. The Commercial Grad's games could completely tie up the telephone system. Everyone, even the family dog it seemed, wanted to be kept informed of the exciting action on the basketball court. Babe Belanger, daughter of telephone's infamous Fred, was a member of the world famous champion Grads team at one time, as were telephone operators Mary Dunn and Babb Dixon. Another on the spot news service was set up for political election results.

Near the end of the roaring twenties more plans were being made for further construction in the telephone department with completion slated for 1930. Who could have foreseen that in a short while the prosperous spirit of the twenties would burst its own balloon and the long depression years would be taken up mainly with the struggle to survive.

Can This Be Love?

Any long-term city telephone employee will tell you, "As long as I can remember, there were rumors flying around about the province buying city telephones." The two administrations were never on amicable terms, and the city telephone department was always suspicious of a takeover by the larger government company.

Soon after Alberta became a province, it began to buy out the Bell Telephone Company interests in the province and start its own telephone network. The new Province of Alberta had been given the Dominion government's telephone rights within Alberta's boundaries. This was welcome news, for no Albertans were happy with the Bell monopoly in the territory, nor did they want to be run by the Dominion government. This elation, at least for Edmontonians, was not to last.

Soon after the Edmonton District Telephone Company was taken over by the city, the municipality negotiated with the government for the sale of its rural interests. The city was glad to be rid of its telephone assets outside Edmonton, because the upkeep would have been more costly than any revenue.

In 1911 when Strathcona and Edmonton agreed to amalgamate, negotiations started between the government and the city for the buy-back of the Strathcona telephone plant. Edmonton assessed the plant and made an offer. The province set their price, which Edmonton thought too high. The province thought the city was stubborn. Edmonton then reassessed the plant and paid the price that the province initially demanded.

When Assistant Superintendent Calhoun pointed out in 1914 that the provincial telephone department was getting a substantial amount of money from long distance tolls which originated in Edmonton, the campaign was on. Why, Edmontonians felt, shouldn't the city get some of the revenue? After all, the total that Alberta Government Telephones (AGT) received from the Trans-Canada Telephone System (TCTS) would be substantially less if Edmonton subscribers did not make use of the long distance system. This toll revenue was not the charge for the long distance calls, but money that the province received from the TCTS for the use of the Alberta system and its equipment. Edmonton received nothing, yet the town was contributing by making use of the long distance facilities and paying the long distance fee.

From 1916 the city began demanding a slice of the pie. AGT turned a deaf ear to the demand, partly because at the time, the company couldn't afford to be generous. The $140,000 a year it received in revenue was so needed that AGT was loath to part with any of it.

When the province had taken over the telephone business they did so on the premise of giving low cost telephone service to all parts of the province. The citizens of Calgary and Red Deer were to receive the same service as someone in the northeast corner of the province. In order to supply these outposts, telephone wires were stretched over miles and miles of uninhabited countryside. With so much equipment and manpower used to supply these far flung phone users, the rural networks were notoriously unprofitable.

Various ideas were put forth as to how to put the department financially back on its feet. Raising rates was one way. AGT did some research and discovered it had, in comparison with other provinces, the lowest rural rates, the lowest toll rates and probably the lowest exchange rates. However a raise in rural rates would have been a political blunder, as the power group in the province was the United Farmers of Alberta. Another proposal was to tax the rural areas that had phone service, but this would have had a negative effect in attracting foreign (out-of-province) capital. Also mentioned was government subsidization of the telephone department.

In 1925 the situation was pronounced desperate. The Honorable Vernor Smith, Minister of Telephones, was mourning the fate in store for AGT. He said it was absolutely imperative that rates be raised.

The next year, in 1926, the government approached the Public Utilities Board to raise the rates $1.00 for businesses, and 50 cents for residential phones. That was poorly received in Calgary where citizens were already upset with the government-run telephone department because they felt that they were subsidizing all the money-gobbling rural lines. With the increase in rates Calgary would be paying more than Edmonton.

While AGT was sinking, the city's profits kept going up and up, and Edmonton kept demanding a share of the toll revenue from the province. AGT started to cast envious eyes on Edmonton's treasure chest.

Talk of buying the city system started in 1927. Edmonton heard the talk and loudly barked, "No Sale." When the province discovered it couldn't get in through the front door, it decided to try another tactic. AGT shouldn't be paying Edmonton some of the toll revenue, it said, Edmonton should be paying AGT a connecting fee for the privilege of using the provincial system. Edmonton didn't think it should pay a penalty for having good business sense. A connecting fee meant a charge over and above the long distance fee. This fee, if paid, would simply mean that Edmonton would be subsidizing the government's unprofitable rural lines. Edmonton would not pay!

Some time passed in silence, then early in 1928, AGT proposed expropriating the city system. The government would purchase the city plant at its book value and, as an added bonus, it would throw in an extra $600,000 for going value. That figure was equal to only five years of telephone surplus and the city could see no profit in selling. When the city refused the offer, the government again demanded payment of a connecting fee in the amount of 20 percent of Edmonton's gross telephone revenue, approximately $100,000 at the time. This amount would naturally grow as the system expanded. Never! said Edmonton.

AGT changed tactics. If Edmonton didn't co-operate, the government would legislate. And it did. In one session of the legislature the government passed an amendment to the public utilities act, giving it, or any other owner of a telephone system, the right to ask a board of public utilities commissioners for power to charge a connecting fee.

The see-saw battle went on. In time the telephone department got a new minister, and he decided to pursue the connecting fee argument.

In May of 1929, the province again submitted a 20 percent connecting fee to the city, and the city submitted a counterclaim for a percentage of toll revenue. The government considered the situation and in November sent the city a letter containing the following points:

1. That the city system should contribute money to AGT so that the provincial body could extend telephone service to new areas and maintain a proper quality of upkeep in the existing province-wide telephone network.

2. The provincial government should be compensated for the services it made available to Edmontonians.

3. The city of Edmonton enjoyed a position not given to Calgary and other centres, and the city of Edmonton should be treated as if it were a part of the provincial system.

In reply, the city outlined the following defense: AGT service was divided into two parts, local and long distance service. For local calls, a flat fee was paid. A subscriber was charged a certain amount per month for the phone rental, whether the subscriber had placed 2 or 2000 calls. For long distance calls, the subscriber was charged according to the length of time on the phone and the distance between the two phones. When Edmonton telephone subscribers used their phones they were charged two ways. No restrictions were placed on local calls. The city charged a flat fee per month, whether the subscriber had made 2 or 2000 calls. When the Edmonton subscriber made a long distance call, he was charged according to the length of time on the line and the distance between the two phones, and that fee was paid directly to AGT. For the use of the provincial toll lines, Edmonton paid the regular fee. But, AGT paid nothing to Edmonton for the use of Edmonton lines. Hardly fair!

According to Mayor Bury and other city officials, the government had only two contentions which would justify a connecting fee:

1. That the cost to AGT of connecting Edmonton telephone subscribers to the AGT - Edmonton toll board was higher than costs of connecting any other city or town to the long distance toll board.

2. That the long distance charges in effect didn't cover the costs incurred by AGT for the calls and AGT would therefore be justified in making an extra charge on everyone in the province on a pro rata basis so part of the long distance cost could be defrayed.

The city quickly ripped the second contention to shreds. Local and long distance service was not interdependent. In the large centres like Calgary and Lethbridge, the equipment operation and maintenance staffs were entirely separate. The city went so far as to state that even in the smaller towns where AGT employees performed both local and long distance service, the costs to each were easily and readily separable.

Even if it were found that the rates for long distance weren't sufficient to support the system, it would be unjust to expect Edmonton residents to subsidize the system when eighty-five percent of the population rarely or never made use of the system. AGT long distance rates should be raised or the system should be overhauled to run on an economical basis, Edmonton said in conclusion.

The Honorable Mr. Brownlee, Minister of Telephones, then suggested that the sequence system of the government would be so beneficial to the city that it would outweigh the effects of paying a hookup fee. The sequence system was a more convenient method of handling a series of toll calls, thus saving time for the caller and the operator. The city reported that of the 16,500 subscribers in the city, only a small fraction of subscribers would ever use the sequence system.

The government also said that because Edmonton was not paying its fair share towards the provincial system, it was retarded in the development of direct connections to the north country and Peace River. To this, Edmonton quoted the following statement made by the government in 1927:

While there is a distinct improvement in business conditions in the north country, the situation there, up to the present, doesn't justify the expenditure which would be necessary to connect up Grande Prairie and Peace River with the main system of the province. Besides being unprofitable, there are apparent physical difficulties of locating repeater stations in suitable locations along the proposed route.

The city claimed that the province would be justified in its annual charge if it could be proved that Edmonton subscribers were receiving benefits from the provincial systems for which no adequate payment was made. Edmonton could be charged if a portion of the revenue from local subscribers in the city, such as Calgary, was being applied to make up a deficit on other parts of the provincial system, and that such application was justifiable and in the best interests of the subscriber. According to the city, the provincial system was making a nice profit from local business in Calgary and other large centers. Rates in Calgary were higher than in Edmonton and the AGT equipment there was more modern and had correspondingly low maintenance costs, therefore the surplus should have been considerably higher than that in Edmonton if the Calgary exchanges were "managed with economy of at all approaching that in vogue in Edmonton." The city asked:

Assuming that there is a considerable surplus from the operation of the Calgary system and other local exchanges in the government system, to what purpose is the surplus applied and can it be shown that the expenditure was equally beneficial to all telephone users in Alberta and should therefore be borne in part by Edmonton users.

The city argument continued. AGT spent huge amounts of money in rural areas where there was sparse population. Those lines were using much more money than they were bringing in, therefore, why develop such unproductive areas and who should pay for the deficits?

Edmonton answered its rhetorical question: AGT undertakes such enterprises because being a government department it must co-operate with other government departments in its efforts to develop the resources of the province. Being able to have a phone in remote districts of the province is quite a drawing card for potential settlers. If Calgary subscribers were to pay a high rate in order that settlers be attracted to unpopulated districts, it would be proper for Edmonton subscribers to pay their share, but it would be just as proper to increase phone rates to build more roads.

The city did extensive research on telephone practices in the United States and came up with a few figures. Of the 10,000 independent phone systems in the United States operating exchanges from a few hundred lines to over 100,000 and all having connections with the long distance networks of large United States companies, in no case were the independent companies paying a connection fee to the companies operating toll networks other than the usual long distance fees.

In cases where public utilities, state and railroad commission boards had jurisdiction over telephone companies, the city found that the practice of raising rates in cities to support unprofitable rural areas wasn't permitted.

The city also pointed out that the Province of Alberta enjoyed connections with many systems in the United States, such as Bell, yet none of these large companies insisted on being paid a connecting fee from the provincial system. All they required was payment for the use of that portion of the line required to complete calls originating from the province. Yet, AGT demanded a connecting fee from Edmonton.

The city then suggested that the province defray the deficit on unprofitable rural lines out of the general taxation of the province or by a levy on wild and undeveloped farm land held for speculation.

The government could see it was up against a strong case and eventually Mr. Brownlee decided, as had Vernor Smith before him, that AGT and the city were engaged in futile negotiations. Mr. Brownlee stated publicly in June of 1930 that the government had no authority and no right to take over the municipal phone system.

Talk of connecting fees and toll revenues was silenced with that announcement and the confrontation reached an impasse.

There was to be a respite of about thirty years, punctuated by the occasional veiled threat of toll revenues and connecting fees. In the meantime, confrontations between the city and the province were limited to the AGT and city telephone golf and curling tournaments.

The Great Depression

For some, the Roaring Twenties came to an abrupt end the day the stock market crashed in New York. For others, the effects were more gradually felt, as the economy slowly ground to a halt. Along with the economic crash came years of adverse weather conditions. Cloudless skies stretched over the prairies as dry warm winds swept down from the mountain ranges, burning up the crops and gardens and blowing dreams away in a cloud of dust. Then came the ravages of the insect pests, army worms and grasshoppers that ate anything that was left. Farm families left their homesteads for better areas, city people lined up for soup and bread. The unemployed started riding the rails in search of work. Many people opened their homes and hearts and shared with those who had nothing. Some people called this decade the "Hungry Thirties," people on the prairies called it the "Dirty Thirties," others called the era the Great Depression.

By 1936, some areas of the country were beginning to feel the burden lighten, and by 1938 the forecast was brighter yet. Then came 1939 and the Second World War. Although it reigned havoc, devastation and misery on a great part of the world, this war also gave the world a new economic lease on life.

In the first year of the decade there were 16,639 phones in Edmonton. With a population of about 75,000, each 100 persons had a total of 22.2 telephones. However 1930 in Edmonton did not give away the secret of the next eight years. Telephone business had continued to boom in the twenties and in 1929 the department was working on the construction of another new exchange. Although the economy was somewhat depressed, the long range outlook was still optimistic and the city went ahead with its telephone expansion. By the beginning of the year, forty men in the department were working day and night on another phase of the increasing telephone network.

The new main exchange building under construction was going to be a two-wire system of the most advanced kind. The central office equipment for the new exchange was supplied by Automatic Electric Company of Chicago, the private branch exchange switchboards were supplied by the Stromberg-Carlson Telephone Manufacturing Company of Toronto, and the telephone instruments were supplied by Automatic Electric and Northern Electric. This equipment filled 5 freight cars and weighed approximately 60 tons. It consisted of 11,000 individual mechanisms inter-connected with cables and wires. The total cost was $545,853, which was slightly more than what Mr. Christie had estimated. Over half of this cost was paid from funds in the telephone department's accumulated reserve account. The installation time of over six months may seem rather lengthy, but understandable considering that 86,400 tiny wires had to be individually spliced by hand.

At midnight June 28, Superintendent Christie, in the presence of Mayor J. Douglas and other civic officials, pulled a little cord attached to a dozen insulator strips and started the cutover of the main telephone exchange to the new two-wire system. In the following years as the city changed each exchange to the two-wire, Christie performed this job over and over, each time trying to break the time record of the previous installation. With the cutover, sixty percent of the city telephones were on the two-wire system and the plan at the time was to complete the changeover within the next two years.

The new exchange had a reserve power set which was a great improvement over the previous one. It consisted of a fifty horsepower gas engine and generator and was sufficient to carry the department along without any other help in case the city electricity supply from the power house was cut off. The power set was also easily adaptable to natural gas in the event that source of energy became available to the city.

The city was also quite impressed with the improvement that the two-wire brought in the fire alarm system. A *Journal* reporter explained the workings of the modern system to the uninformed:

When a subscriber dials "100" the mechanical brain says "fire department" but at the same time it says, "maybe this is a false alarm, I must tell these humans so that they can trace it back." The mechanical brain rings a bell and causes a red light to flash on. An attendant at once leaps to the instrument and a few rapid glances gives him the number of the telephone from which the call came. When the mechanical brain received the "100" stimuli from a pay station, it not only says "fire and perhaps a false alarm," but adds, "this person is doing a public service and should not be charged five cents for doing it, he must have his money returned as soon as the call has been traced," and the five cent piece comes shooting out of the instrument in the far off pay station.

The new system was also able to keep accurate accounts for the provincial and city telephone systems, with respect to long distance calls made through pay stations. The system also recorded every local call made from a pay station.

At this time the city finally started to feel the full impact of the depression. There was no longer any possibility of changing the entire city to the two-wire system by 1932. Plans were shelved. People were not getting new phones, they were giving them up, and the forecast was gloomy. The telephone became a luxury. Food, clothing and shelter were more essential, and if a person could barely afford a wall, he could hardly afford a phone to hang on it.

Even if Edmonton had not been directly affected by the depression, its indirect consequences would still have made further telephone expansion unlikely. The condition of the bond market at this time resulted in high interest rates, and the city could not have afforded to borrow the needed money.

The department at this time gave citizens every opportunity to keep their telephones. Before 1933, subscribers had to pay their phone bills three months in advance. Effective July 1, 1933, subscribers paid their bills monthly. A discount of five percent would be given if the bill was paid within the first ten days of the month. No discount was given after that and the phone would be cut off if the bill was not paid by the twentieth day. The adoption of the monthly system helped many people keep their phones, as it was much easier to pay one month's rent at one time.

By 1934, the number of phones was 15,049, a drop of 1599 phones in four years. The financial statements for the years 1930 through 1933 had showed a deficit. Although city telephones was suffering, Alberta Government Telephones (AGT) was in worse financial straits for it had the tremendous costs of upkeep for lines that stretched over miles of prairie to reach phones that were sitting idle on the walls because the owners couldn't afford to reconnect them and AGT couldn't afford to remove them. The *Calgary Herald* observed at this point that "events have proven that Edmonton was right in keeping its system separate, and Calgary wrong in going with the government."

In January 1935, the city announced some good news. For the first time in four years, the phone department — hardest hit of the city utilities — reported an increase in the gross revenue. Another interesting piece of news was that the telephone population had increased. Edmonton had added 300 more phones in 1934. Since the telephone department was considered a reliable barometer of business, a flicker of hope was rekindled and optimists began to preach the return of better times.

By the beginning of 1935 there was renewed talk of continuing the modernization program of the telephone department which had started in 1920 with the first two-wire system. The final two exchanges on the list were the west end and north end exchanges. At the time their performance was very poor, and the only way that efficiency could be improved was by eliminating the three-wire system entirely and replacing it with a two-wire system. Such a venture would require a substantial capital outlay of $500,000.

By February of 1936 the modernization of the two exchanges was, according to Bob Christie, urgently needed. His plans were to change the west end or number "8" exchange within the year to the modern two-wire equipment. The money needed to transform that exchange would come out of the department's reserve fund. More and more people wanted telephone service and the current subscribers were clamoring for the new type of phone that came with the two-wire system.

As Christie was talking of modernization, Montreal was making a study of Canadian telephone habits. It reported that Canadians did more telephoning than any other country and that Edmontonians did more telephoning than any other Canadian city.

This was a point of pride for some residents, for this huge amount of telephoning signified their sociability, business acumen, sophistication and ability to afford a phone. Perhaps Mr. Christie felt that his publication would help city council loosen its pocket-book a bit.

Near the end of the year, telephone figures were released showing that the department was growing steadily. The *Journal* observed: "The continued steady increase in the number of telephones in service in Edmonton is further evidence of the return of better times, for the 'necessary luxury' is a good barometer of improved business conditions all around."

In 1937 the city changed the format for the telephone directory to 8¾ inches by 11 inches, which was standard for other North American telephone companies.

Christie wanted to make another improvement. The south side service would be at its capacity by September or October, and further telephone applications would have to go on a waiting list. It was imperative, Christie maintained, for immediate provision for the extension of facilities. Council agreed, and an item of $18,000 was included under capital expenditure for 1937 to cover the extension of the south side exchange.

City telephones was given another long awaited green light in June when a proposal to modernize the north and west end exchanges, at a total cost of not more than $440,000, was approved by city council. A by-law was passed authorizing work up to a cost of $205,000 to start that year. New equipment also had to be ordered for these exchanges as soon as possible, since a shortage of equipment before the end of 1939 was predicted. The equipment would require eighteen months for manufacture and installation after the order was placed. The equipment in these exchanges, in use for up to twenty-nine years, was obsolete. Parts were no longer being manufactured, so when equipment broke down makeshift repairs had to be done. Telephone complaints in those two exchanges were numerous.

In July the purchase of 2800 lines of phone equipment for the west end exchange and 2500 lines for the north exchange was approved by council. The west end exchange equipment was to cost $114,380 and would be delivered within fourteen months. The two-wire central office switching equipment was purchased from Canadian Telephone and Supplies Ltd. of Toronto, and it would be installed by the supplier. The equipment for the north end exchange, tagged at

$106,306, was ordered from a British firm with completion and delivery to be made within twenty months.

By August the excavation was started for the new $32,000 north Edmonton telephone exchange located at 89 Street and 118 Avenue. This building was to be completed by the end of November and installation of the equipment would be finished by the end of 1938. The new north exchange building was to replace the existing building at 101 Street and 112 Avenue. The old exchange would then be used as a store room and a workshop. Years later, when north stores near NAIT was built, the 112 Avenue building became the City Archives.

In November of 1937 the citizens of Ottawa got their first taste of automatic equipment, 29 years after Edmonton. In the latest telephone survey, Edmonton boasted 1 phone for every 5 people, while the average for Canada was 11 per 100 and the United States 13 per 100.

In the first of the new year, the telephone department took its own survey. A questionnaire was sent out to the west end residents concerning new phone equipment. Seventy-five percent of replies favored the wall monophone over the old wooden box. The wall monophones were attractive for the householder and the added expense didn't seem to bother the subscriber. The department didn't mind either as it meant more revenue.

The first step in the west end changeover was to move a portion of the existing old three-wire apparatus so that sufficient floor space would be available for putting in the new equipment. After the old apparatus was relocated, the interior of the building was renovated and the motor generator rooms were built in the basement. While installation of central office equipment was going on, work was progressing on splicing underground cables connecting outside lines with new equipment, but leaving a temporary connection with the old equipment. In September of '38, the new instruments were placed in subscribers' homes in the west end. Until the switchover, the subscribers had two phones in their homes.

The last Sunday in November, at 2 AM, the changeover started. It took only seven minutes and was the fastest cutover since the modernization program had started. Twenty-eight operators at the west end exchange cut off the old phones and a separate operation had to be performed for each of the 2800 lines to start the new equipment in service. This involved yanking out 2800 toothpicks, which as nonconductors were used to plug out the new equipment while the old equipment was still in use. As each toothpick was pulled out, each new contact was completed.

That Sunday, the city was flooded with calls. They were recorded at a rate of 4500 per hour between 11:30 AM and 2 PM, which was more than four times heavier than normal Sunday traffic. There was clearer line reception reported and out of the entire 2800 lines affected by the cutover, only one was found to be out of service, and that situation was remedied within two minutes.

For the next two weeks telephone workmen were busy removing old sets from west end homes. It would be impossible to sell the old equipment, as at the time only one city in North America — Richmond, Indiana — was still on the old three-wire system and it had already contracted for the two-wire type. The only other way to get some money out of old equipment was to extract the platinum from the instruments.

By January of '39, installation of 2400 new telephones in the north end or "7" exchange began. Later that year, as the west end exchange came perilously close to being overcrowded again, council passed an additional $32,000 for station equipment capable of handling 800 new individual services and for 300 new lines of equipment in the west end. Some of the equipment was again ordered from Britain, even though the city was well aware that the tension in Europe could result in a delayed delivery date.

There was a political crisis in April that caused a three-week halt to a British shipment of central office equipment for the north end exchange that had been ordered in 1937.

In September tension in Europe was high, and Edmonton was thinking of alternate plans if the 60 phones recently ordered from Britain could not be sent. They were to arrive in the spring of 1940, at the same time that 300 phones built in the United States were to arrive.

The north end exchange had been completed in June and all lines were switched over to the new two-wire equipment, completing the changeover of the whole city to the two-wire. This particular operation took ten minutes and consisted of pulling toothpicks out of the 2400 lines.

The complete change to the two-wire resulted in greatly increased efficiency. By November of '39 service complaints received by the department had been cut to one-tenth of what they were thirteen years before. The average was two complaints per phone per year. (In 1926 the average had been fifteen.) The great majority of complaints were for simple things like inquiring about a constantly busy signal, or getting a wrong number twice in a row.

R. C. Brown was another fortunate man hired in the early years of the depression. He was foreman of the west end exchange for years.

Herb C. Caldwell started as an office boy in that decade. During this time Herb would collect paystations; it took one afternoon a week. This was during the days that businesses had to guarantee a cash flow of $5 a week from the pay stations on their premises or make up the difference. Herb was a keen pool shark. During the war years he was also an expert at getting things that were rationed. Whatever one's heart desired, Herb could get and would gladly trade with his fellow workers. In 1939 Herb got involved in the International Brotherhood of Electrical Workers, Local 1007 and became the first business manager of the local from 1953 to 1965. In 1954 Herb was part of a trade mission to some Arab countries, and when he came back to city telephones he was safety and training officer. Even after Herb retired in 1975, he still went up to the main exchange many noon hours to play hearts with some of the boys.

Further hiring was minimal until the late thirties. In '38 four more people joined — Arnold Logan, Morgan MacDonald, Jack Tolmie and William McCombs.

Arnold Logan became a journeyman switchman and could be relied on to answer any number of technical questions. Jack Tolmie probably spent more time in the rack room than any other man in the city's history. He had started with CTS as a cableman's helper, left shortly after to join the air force, then played the saxaphone in the RCAF band in Ottawa for three-and-a-half years. Jack had started his musical career in 1927 when he joined John Michael's (Mike's News Stand) Newsboy's Band. Later Jack had his own combo and played at various places throughout the city. He also raised mink for a number of years. When Jack came back to CTS after the war he moved to the rack room. Jack's retirement from the department in October of 1978 was described fondly by some fellow old-timers as the removal of one of the permanent fixtures of the Churchill Square Office.

Bill McCombs spent most of his time in the telephone department working on installations. He could probably tell you how all the buildings were wired. McCombs was easily recognizable — a man with a phone permanently attached to one ear and the smoke of three or four cigarettes fogging up his part of the room. McCombs loved duck hunting. Each year he and a friend would load up their gear and an ample supply of refreshments and head off to their favorite slough. The boys would always come back empty-handed — that is, minus both ducks and beverages. McCombs had started as an installer and left the department in the position of service engineer.

Morgan MacDonald was installation foreman. He is remembered by some of the men as the one who put the drop through the ladder, which in layman's language means that while stringing the service wire from the nearest telephone pole to the house being worked on, Morgan strung the wire through the ladder he was standing on. When he attempted to remove the ladder he discovered his mistake and had to spend some overtime minutes cutting and splicing the wire back together again. Morgan was always losing his toe rubbers. When he and his sidekick Wally Jowett would enter a home to do some work, Wally would kick Morgan's rubbers downstairs when he wasn't looking. Morgan was often late getting home.

In 1939 three more long timers joined the ranks — G. Engley, Art Bamber and D. (Ivan) Green.

Ivan Green had one outstanding characteristic, he had the shiniest shoes in the whole department. It could have just rained mud, but Ivan's shoes glistened. During the royal visit in 1939 Ivan had to work in a heat wave installing a telephone cable from the old CNR station to the royal car parked on the north side of the CNR tracks.

Gord Engley was a line foreman and used to be the pack rat of the old heavy gang. Gord was also quite a card shark.

Art Bamber was another lineman of the old school. He became supervisor of construction. Art had a mischievous side to him and was a good prankster because he had such an innocent-looking face. Because of this, he seldom received his just reward for a lot of the skullduggery that went on. There was the time that Art nailed Jock Benny's brand new rubbers to the ceiling. Jock looked all over for those rubbers and put the blame on everyone in sight except the real culprit.

Fred Belanger, one of the legends of Edmonton Telephones, was another one for nailing rubbers or tools to immobile objects. He was pretty good too at removing immobile objects. The story is told that one night during the thirties, Belanger and Jack (Septimus) Baker removed a grave monument, reputed to be an angel, from a local cemetery or place of worship. They painted the statue black and put it on a relative's grave. It is also said of that escapade that Baker, his cohort, developed a hernia lifting the angel onto the getaway truck.

Belanger was a small Frenchman, a tough ex-boxer. He always wore the same red toque and work clothes and always carried a pair of cableman's snippers. The occasional time that he removed this paraphernalia and dressed up in a nice raccoon coat and hat, he was almost unrecognizable. Belanger liked a good joke and capitalized on his special mixture of French Canadian and English to give his friends a good laugh. A standing Belanger joke was to send three men up and pole and then yell "half come down." Phrases like "throw the horse over the fence some hay" would also get a chuckle or two.

Belanger was a good foreman and could have drawn from memory a map of the city telephone cable. He was instrumental in the department getting hydraulic rod pushers. Fred was also a real card shark. Fast of hand and foot, he didn't think anything of depriving some fellow of a few of his dollars by pulling a fast one, but in the next breath would offer that money to anyone in need.

The office staff stayed much the same during this time. Lizzy Campbell and Jean Duncan were still in the directory department winning praise for their work. The city commissioners said that no men ever had been found as efficient as those women. With scores of thousands of chances to make errors, their percentage of mistakes was lower than two per issue, and often they finished several issues in a row without making any mistakes at all.

The telephone operator of the thirties was still plagued with numerous calls that had nothing to do with numbers. They still got questions like "How do you coddle an egg", "When will the comet be visible tonight," or "When is the government going to start paying dividends." The operators at central did get rid of a nuisance in the early part of the decade. They would have to answer "960", the time call, at least 9000 times a day. The majority of calls came from children just before and after school and during the noon hour. When the new main exchange was cut over to the two-wire in 1930 the time service was abolished.

The information operator's methods went through a change. The operators now had access to whirling directories where thousands of names and numbers were catalogued on removable and up-to-date tabulation slips. By the end of the decade there were eight information operators who tried to stick to routine answers for calls inquiring about changed numbers and removals, and less time answering questions like "What is the capital of Afghanistan."

The unsung heroes of the department were still coping with the weather. Ten courageous and hardy men were employed on the outside staff of the department. To these men of the "suicide squad" fell the duty of climbing poles in sub-zero weather to repair broken wires and other outside plant equipment — bare fingered to boot. In addition to the outside men, there was another group of four men who would string new telephone wires into newly built homes. Their work was outside about 50 percent of the time. Five trouble shooters were also employed checking on connections, testing circuits and splicing cable. Fortunately for members of the cable gang, most outdoor trouble in the department came during the spring, after the ravages of winter left the equipment in a weakened state.

Wages weren't anything to write home about in the thirties. In 1929 the agreement accepted by the International Brotherhood of Electrical Workers never did materialize because of the depression. Wages didn't rise again until 1940, and at that time the men made the same wage they had made in 1928. Hiring was limited, and in many cases if a person quit he wasn't replaced, instead his work was divided among the remaining workers.

Many people found that they could no longer afford the luxury of a telephone. Scores of phones were removed, and sometimes so many phones had to be disconnected that the crews didn't have the time to physically remove the set. So the phones remained, hanging on the wall until the upsurge that the war brought to the economy allowed their owners to reconnect them.

A. Taylor,
*President and General
Manager, Edmonton & District
Telephone Company
1885-1904*

G. Stanton,
*Manager of the telephone system
when taken over by the City in
1905.*

J.E. Lowry,
*Superintendent, Telephone
Department, City of Edmonton
1915-1921*

R. Christie,
Superintendent, Telephone
Department, City of Edmonton
(became City of Edmonton
Telephone System, 1940)
1921-1951

C.E. Brown, *City of*
Superintendent, City of
Edmonton Telephone System
1951-1965

S. Hampton,
Superintendent
(General Manager)
City of Edmonton
Telephone System
January 1966 - January 1967

D. Burrows,
General Manager,
'edmonton telephones'
(name changed March, 1967)
October 1967 - December 1972

J. Pulford,
General Manager,
'edmonton telephones'
February 1973 - March 1976

G.K. Foster,
General Manager,
'edmonton telephones'
July 1976 -

*Arthur Ormsby, the Edmonton district telephone
company's first electrician.
Photo courtesy Mrs. Chester Hale.*

*Standing is Jennie Lauder, first telephone operator,
sitting is her sister Margaret, later Mrs. Art Ormsby.
Photo taken in 1891, courtesy Miss Norine Lauder.*

Working on the main frame in the main exchange, around 1929, are top to bottom: Al Eager, Dave Muir, L. Dineen, and Alf Lewis.

*Ben Davison, Chris Earl, Lil Whitla, Meta Robinson and
Minnie Tebbutt by the main exchange in 1918.
Photo courtesy Mrs. B. Davison.*

*The City Telephone System hockey team in 1922.
Back row left to right: Jack Rutherford, Fred Rayner,
Carl Tomlinson, Wilf Kenney, Al Eager, Harvey Grierson.
Front row: Ben Davison, Buster Brown, Glen Cornes,
Harry Fawns.*

*Telephone girls Anna Stoeser and Lil Garden on the city
telephone float, beside the main exchange. 1926.*

The original test board at the main exchange.

'edmonton telephones' first administration building was
built in the teens, under W.R. Griffiths' superintendency.
It was expanded in the '20's, then remodelled in the 1940's.
It is now known as the Churchill Exchange, but still houses
Directory Assistance.

*Information and trouble girls at the main exchange in
1915. Top to bottom, left to right: L. Gibson,
Jeanie Maxwell, Celeb Davis, Mamie Cairns,
Nellie Turner, Flossie Jietz, Anna Stoeser.*

The "information girls", Directory Assistance, still on manual systems in the early 1960's.

Today's "information girls and boys" are now helped by electronics, with a computerized information base and visual display terminals. Left to right, Isobel Peters, Gwen Thompson, Jackie Ihrig, Joan Shaben, Inez Ewald and Walter Edwards are a few of the over 110 staff handling customer number requests on a 24-hour basis.

D.F. Burrows, 'et' General Manager, receives a plaque honoring 'et's' first place honors in the straight truck class for color and design in the 1968 National Private Truck Fleet Marking Contest. Presenting the award to him on behalf of the American Trucking Association is Conference Chairman Warren R. Ross, their 1968 Conference Chairman.

*'et's' 1976-77 staff hockey team of marketing and sales
(dark uniforms) and others. Marketing and sales staff are
sponsored by Northern Telcom and take on all challengers.
Left to right first row are: Tom Burn, Larry Dickenson,
Al Hawgood, Bruce Meyer, Ed Burchmore, Roger Graff,
John Pierce, Roy Westbrook, Orvall Burchby,
Bill Hodgson;
second row: Ken Parsons, Graham Strachan,
Jim McLaughlin, Doug Hope, "Scotty" Wilson,
Jack Rudichuk, Brian Hague, Hank Zurch, Mike White,
Rod Proudfoot, Denys Lewis, Gary Wilson, Ron Sharpe,
Dale McIlhargey and Jim O'Donnel. While Jack Rudichuk
works for A.G.T., he was considered a good catch.
John Pierce and Rod Proudfoot, non-employees are
actually the husband and brother of staff member Dianne
Pierce. "Scotty" Wilson, another non-'et'er was taken on as
a mascot.*

*Mayor Terry Cavanagh, left, and 'et' General Manager
Ken Foster officially open Edmonton's first phone store,
the Centennial Shopping Centre "Phone Exchange"
June 16, 1977.*

'edmonton telephones' was heavily involved in providing telecommunications services for the XI Commonwealth Games in 1978. Here, Audry Welby, Sandy Kindley, Laura Roesler and Nellie Anquist ('et' Chief Operator) provided information services during the actual games.

"Light Rapid Transit", became a reality in 1978. 'et' installed closed circuit television, public address systems in the stations, the PBX and a unique radio system for the tunnels. From left to right, Dennis Villeneuve, responsible for the P/A system; Neil McDougall, marketing consultant; Ken Parsons, project supervisor; and Gary Boisvert (seated), responsible for the radio system, try out the communications console.

1979 'et' executive from left: Fred Windwick, General Plant Manager; Harry Rogers, Chief Engineer; Hap Elliott, Acting Buildings, Vehicles and Supplies Manager; Ken Foster, General Manager; Stan Shpiel, Acting Organization Development and Financial Control Manager; and Paul Trawick, General Commercial Manager.

The Feverish Forties

Canada was feeling the consequences of the war in Europe by the beginning of 1940. Unlike the previous world war, in which city residents had given up their phones, the lines of subscribers at the doors of the telephone office were getting longer and longer. The problem was a shortage of vital materials. Telephone equipment for six hundred lines for the north and west ends of the city had been ordered from a British firm in April of 1939. However the materials for the order were diverted to war production, and the telephones were delayed.

Edmontonians could get new phone connections only through changes within the city. By November of '40, the waiting list for phones had reached 60. In December the department received the welcome words that the equipment was on its way from Britain. When it finally reached Edmonton in March of '41, to a waiting list that had grown to 200, the British were praised for their ability to deliver the goods despite the war. An additional 1000 phones had been ordered in December from Britain for the north and south exchanges at a cost of $66,884, but because of the war this order could not be filled and it was reordered from Brockvile, Ontario, at a cost of $91,000.

While Edmontonians were plagued with communication delays, farmers in the area surrounding Edmonton were getting plugged in. The 2000 old phones, sold as salvage to an Edmonton firm in 1940, were picked up by the farmers for next to nothing.

A number of people were hired in the early part of the decade to replace some telephone employees who had joined the services and to handle the extra work load created by the upsurge in installations. The plant department in particular increased in numbers.

The first to join the City Telephone System (CTS) in 1940 was George Sloane. George, the chief tester who replaced Cliff Butterworth, was exacting and fastidious in his work. For a time Sloane was in charge of rationing pencils, and in order to get a brand new one, a person had to turn in his stub. George later moved into engineering and became outside plant engineer.

Neil Tomilson joined the gang in '41. Neil was a PBX inspector and started the department's hobby of building one's own house.

Jim Watson also started that year. Jim was always in top notch shape, and not only was Jim the fastest coffee drinker around, he was probably the fastest walker. No one could keep up with Jim, even men many years his junior. Jim delighted in pulling the following gag. He would load up his men with heavy equipment then run up the stairs, simultaneously issuing orders to his men who were frantically trying to keep up with him. Naturally none of the fellows heard what he said and if they had, by the time they had reached the top of the stairs their exhausted condition would have prevented them from carrying out the orders anyway. Jim could go full speed ahead for fourteen hours a day without the slightest trace of fatigue.

Doug Carmichael, line and cable supervisor, came to Edmonton from Detroit. Harry Sackman, City Telephone's cigarette moocher, joined in 1942, as did Robert McCue. Bob joined the installation department when three trucks serviced the entire city.

Ralph Cable started as an apprentice switchman, became foreman of the Woodcroft then the Churchill Square exchange and was promoted to chief switchman in charge of all the exchanges before moving into central office engineering in 1970. Ralph retired from telephones in 1974 but took up switching in his basement. What had started out as a centennial project for Ralph and his son turned into a fascinating hobby. The team collected electric trains, souped them up with throttle controls and switching gear and added some classy scenery.

Clarence Cruse, another electric train fanatic, also started in '42. Clarence was in the outside plant department as a cable splicer.

Pete Winters joined that year as a cable splicer's helper. Harry Ward and Tom Paton were night operators for a number of years.

Tom Wyley, an engineering technician, started near the first of that year and is now the employee with the most seniority in the department. Tom is another great city telephone carpenter. His china cabinets display his craftsmanship and his stone fireplace has won many admiring comments. Tom took his time building that fireplace. When Tom and family headed off to the lake cottage on a weekend, a different route would be taken each time, the purpose being to keep an eye on the countryside for suitable fieldstone. The trips would take up to three hours and sometimes, by the time the cottage was in view, the Wyley car would almost be touching the ground from the weight of the stones in the trunk.

Jimmy Blair, second to Tom in seniority, now works in the repair shop as an installer. Jimmy joined the navy shortly after he started with telephones and returned to the department after the war. A great athlete, Jim played Class A ball in the United States for some time and is now a very active curler.

George Buckham started during the third year of the war. George had worked in Saskatchewan erecting phone lines and spent some time with AGT before joining city telephones as a repairer and installer. A big man, George looked like a bear climbing the telephone poles. According to one fellow worker, George had fantastic ideas and explanations for "things that hadn't happened and never would." He was a captivating individual always ready to entertain with a humorous anecdote.

Following close on the heels of George was John Stanley Morrison Wright. J. S. M. was a handy-man, a jack of all trades. He would do the department's carpentry work, plumbing and any other fix-it job that was required. When he wasn't working for telephones he was riding a local ambulance.

Another problem that arose in 1942 was the government's restrictions on the use of nonferrous metals. No civilian telephone requiring more than 125 feet of wire could be installed — and so the waiting list grew. There were enough phones on hand to meet the demand, but the other essential materials could not be secured. By February of '43, there were three hundred persons waiting for phones. The telephone department then announced that because of the wartime shortage of copper and the need to conserve vital material, these Edmontonians would not get their phones until after the war, unless there was a big reduction in the number of subscibers. Christie certainly wasn't a popular man after making that announcement, and other telephone employees, when out and about, were just a little reluctant to discuss their occupation.

Companies which used to manufacture telephone equipment were ninety percent converted to war work. These manufacturers had restrictions placed on them regarding the manufacture of telephone equipment. They could supply domestic telephone equipment only for maintenance work, new construction would not be permitted. If essential military need was proven, the plants would supply the equipment, but it had to be on a priority basis. Essential industries like fire and police departments and hospitals were also supplied.

At this time, civilians had to have a pretty good reason in order to get a phone. An essential need had to be proven, and many subscribers tried to get a phone in their residence by claiming business reasons. Two very popular occupations at this time were babysitting and dressmaking. Other people cited a medical reason in their application, either by being a member of the medical profession or by being completely reliant on it. During the war the department assigned double zero numbers to people reliant on the medical profession. "Pregnancy numbers" as they were called, were issued for three-month periods. Straight residential applications were granted in order of priority.

By July of '43, the city was swarming with Americans. Since the start of the war the telephone department had installed thirty-one private branch telephone exchange boards at air schools and other installations for the United States government. With the exception of the United States army, all telephone equipment to the United States government offices and American contractors was owned by the city. By the summer of '43, the city felt that the department had passed the hump in the rush to supply the numerous American installations put up in 1942. The department had been taxed to the limit in keeping up with repairs on equipment and keeping the telephones in working order.

The telegraph-telephone line from Edmonton to Fairbanks, Alaska, being built by the U.S. Army Signal Corps, was almost complete in August of '43. The 2020-mile line linking Alaska with Edmonton was to be in operation by the first of October. At the time it was the longest open wire telephone line in the world. As many as 2000 messages a day were coming down the wires already in use between Edmonton and Whitehorse.

When the line was completed, 22 repeater stations each requiring about 50 tons of equipment were in operation. There were 21 lines of communication, 12 direct telegraph circuits, 2 direct-current telegraph circuits and 7 talking circuits, all over 4 strands of copper wire.

In 1944, 90 percent of the output of plants manufacturing phone equipment was still being used for war purposes. The phone shortages in the city were severe, especially in the north end of the city. The city's 170 paystations were doing quite a business and 20 more were on order.

In January of '44, the telephone department announced a breakthrough. It had purchased $65,505 worth of phone equipment; 300 lines for the main exchange and 220 for the west end exchange. The order, backed by a permit from the comptroller of construction at Ottawa, was with the Automatic Electric Company of Canada who guaranteed delivery within eight months. As there was no room in the main exchange to house the equipment on order, discussions began on plans to build an addition to the Churchill Square building.

By June of '44, there were more than 1000 residential applications on file and there was concern that the shortage of equipment would soon affect business establishments. In September, the city bought three new machines in anticipation of a changeover to the stub system of billing which was to increase the efficiency in the accounting department. The machines would eliminate three staff positions and result in an annual salary saving of $4800. The city telephone department had taken ten years to join power and water in sending out its monthly billing on common dates.

Unlike all other city departments, city telephones did not suffer from lack of manpower to do the available work. Many of the skilled technicians in the department were classed as "irreplaceable" and therefore exempt from the services. Also, since there hadn't been much hiring in the thirties, by the time the war came many of the fellows were too old to qualify for war duty. If more men were needed, well there were always qualified people around not averse to becoming a member of the city telephone department, and a few of them came in '44.

Al Josey started as a zone clerk in May. Computers and calculators weren't available then and most of the billing was individually stamped and hand written. It was a tedious job and sometimes very time consuming. Superintendent Christie was a perfectionist and everything had to balance, down to the penny. Josey remembers having to spend one weekend looking for one cent that had somehow lost itself on the balance sheets. Alex later became president of Local 52 of the Civic Service Union, later president of the Alberta division, and regional vice-president in Canada.

George Glanville came in the summer and stayed for 34 years. He spent his time in the drafting department, retiring in the position of schedules, records and drafting supervisor.

William Padavel joined the line gang and J. C. Smith became a night operator. Bill, later foreman of the line gang, was known as the bread man of city telephones since he liked to pick up a fresh loaf every day.

Bert Billingsley started out as a ledger clerk in '45 and worked his way up to zone clerk. He then moved into payroll and customer services, becoming supervisor of commercial practises, and in 1960 was made commercial manager. Bert was very hard working and conscientious.

Wally Watt started out as an office boy and in '48 joined Billingsley, Josey and Reddick Mills as a zone clerk. Shortly after, Orville Stevenson came to work as Wally's assistant. Ed Wensley, a 35-year veteran, and Ewart Johnson were also in the commercial department. Ewart was traffic manager at one time when information and repair were together.

Ken Wilde for years was the dispatcher on the test desk. Ken was a diminutive person but had a big booming voice, which was often effective in scaring the person at the other end of the line into compliance.

Then Eddie (Jock) Bennie came along. He was a happy-go-lucky dapper fellow, tiny but tough as old leather. Eddie once caught the full force of a steel sledge hammer in his face and remained standing.

Dunc Foster and Jim Barnett were among the first returning war veterans to join the department. Dunc had been a bombadier in the air force. Always a prankster, Dunc has a habit of springing the punch line of a joke just as his listeners had taken a gulp of coffee. Dunc took a duty-sponsored class on retirement in '78 and had the city officer a bit perplexed when he asked if he could still retire if he failed the course. Dunc probably has the oldest pet in the department. It's a 67-year-old pet rock, taken from one of the columns in the Revillon building.

Jim Barnett, also an air force veteran, started out as a switchman, moved to the test desk and became chief tester, did some PABX maintenance and is now a technical officer in services engineering. Jim Barnett was the host the night of the famous radio caper. One evening Ross McCutcheon, Bob Gibb, Dunc Foster and Alf Issacs were having a get-together at the Barnett home. At one point they decided that Barnett's long-legged radio would look much better as a table model. The radio was a bit shaky and the idea was to steady it somewhat by adjusting the legs. The boys maneuvered the host couple out of the living room, procured an old rip saw from the basement and went to work. By the time the evening was at an end, the poor radio didn't have any legs at all. The Barnetts took it in good fun, Jeanette Barnett claiming she likes it much better now.

When the Americans pulled out of the city in 1945, people thought they would be able to take over the American phone equipment, but existing agreements between the two countries required the Americans to take their equipment with them. These citizens were further angered to find out that some people just moving into the city or neighborhood were taking over phones left by previous tenants. As in the twenties, the new people would pay the phone bills made out to the previous owners, distribute the number to their friends, and hope that people who had been waiting since '39 for a phone would never know. But they did find out and were hopping mad, blaming the department for its inefficiency.

That year, plans were finalized to construct a $175,000 addition to the phone building on 102 Avenue and 100 Street. With the start of construction, one of the city's oldest brick landmarks, the old labour hall, was to be demolished. The addition, to be built out of reinforced concrete with a stone facing, would double the size of the exchange. It was predicted that the ultimate capacity of 10,000 lines would not be used up for 20 to 25 years.

By fall the work on the main exchange was behind schedule. There had been delays in delivering the materials, and there had been a shortage of skilled labor in the summer. During the winter of '45 to '46, eight gas furnaces burned inside the building so bricklayers and carpenters could be kept on the job. These furnaces and a high protecting wall of pine boards and tarpaulin enabled the work to continue. That was the only big construction job in Edmonton to go through the winter.

In October of '46, the Canadian government paid $1,700,000 for the Edmonton to Whitehorse segment of the line built by the American army.

In 1947 the waiting list was up to 4000, a year later it reached 5000. In May of '48, approval was given to build an addition to the south side exchange at a cost of $67,000. Work started in the fall.

The main exchange was also completed. It had taken four years. An additional, 4800 phones were to be added by the end of the year and another 2480 in 1949;

After that the department hoped it would be caught up with demand. With the completion of the building, 25 members of the staff moved to new quarters.

During the war the shortage of phone equipment had been due to a shortage of necessary materials used in manufacturing central office equipment. After the war there was so much labor unrest that supplies still weren't getting in fast enough. Another obstacle was the shortage of telephone cable. In 1946, 48 miles of cable were laid, in 1947 only 10 miles of cable were installed. The growth in Edmonton was phenomenal at this time, for after the Leduc oil strike immigrants came from other provinces to Alberta, the land of opportunity and black gold. New subdivisions were springing up but city money was still tight. Had the department been able to obtain all the equipment it needed, the council probably wouldn't have approved the large expenditures.

As the list got longer, there were more rumors of favoritism. Superintendent Christie repeatedly denied the rumors saying: "We have a definite schedule of priority set up and this is followed to the letter. As soon as equipment is available it is installed, and as far as possible business phones get priority."

The telephone department tried to sooth the irritated public. The busy signal was changed from a buzz to a higher toned beep, making it much easier on the nerves. The department talked of its plans to increase the telephone population by 8780 in '49 with extensions to the north and west end exchanges. Although there was also an indication of a rate raise, Christie reminded subscribers that the city's telephone rates were still the lowest of any major city in Canada.

The second half of the decade was busy in the telephone department. Men were coming back from the war swelling the labor market.

Major M. F. Browse had been with the 13 Division Signals and the Loyal Edmonton Regiment. Marshall was promoted to officer commanding the 13 district signals, RCCS when the headquarters of the unit was transferred from Calgary to Edmonton in 1945.

Charlie McKeage, Bill McLaughlin and Bob Gibb had been in the air force, Jim McKernan and J. H. (Pug) Young came from the navy and Lloyd Brown from the army.

Bill McLaughlin started as a central office man, became a senior member of the engineering branch, was promoted to general plant manager, then general services manager, a position which he held until his death.

When Bob Gibb got out of the air force, he took an electrical course before joining city telephones. He was on the test desk with Ross McCutcheon, Dunc Foster and Jim Barnett when Cliff Butterworth was still in charge. It seems that these four often gave Cliff a hard time. Gibb was recalled from retirement in the fall of '78 to head the team installing the automatic meter reading test units into the Millwoods area.

Jim McKernan, of construction, made climbing a pole a fine art. "It was poetry in motion to see Jim climb a pole," one fellow worker commented. Jim is a great athlete despite his handicap. A number of years ago he lost his left arm to cancer, but can still knock 'em dead on the golf course with an average 86 in 18 holes. He won a golf tournament for amputees in Augusta, Georgia and is probably the best one-armed golfer in western Canada. Lloyd Brown lost his right arm to shrapnel while fighting in Italy during the war. Lloyd has a good attitude too, joking that he and Jim buy gloves together.

Then along came James Harvey (Pug) Young. Big and burly, Pug was the dreaded bear of the ice in the forties and fifties; some say he could have made the NHL. Pug would knock a guy down hard but he'd always stop to pick him up again. Pug played with the Lethbridge Maple Leafs for three-and-a-half years, then played with the old Flyers when they won the Allen Cup in the fifties. Those were the days when people used to line up to get tickets for hockey games. Pug also coached the Oil Kings for a few years and along with manager Leo LeClerc helped take the Oil Kings to the championships year after year. Christie wasn't too happy about Pug's hockey playing in the forties. He'd warn Pug that if it interfered with his job performance it would be "goodbye Charlie." There were a few mornings when that warning kept Pug from staying at home to nurse his injuries.

Hugh Dunnighan was a forty-sixer and the philosopher of CTS. If anyone had a problem, Hugh would be the person to see. He was also pretty good at arguing both sides of a coin. The only person to leave Hugh the slightest bit puzzled was Doug Burrows, the general manager of telephones in the late sixties and early seventies.

In 1947 more war veterans joined the department — Sid Bryant and Ted Bennett from the navy, Ross McCutcheon, Roy McBurney and Alf Issacs from the air force and Ken Sherwin from the army.

Ted Bennett had been on a destroyer that was searching for German subs after the surrender. They located four, the last one off the coast of Newfoundland heading for New York Harbor. They hauled it into Shelbourne, Nova Scotia and were quite surprised to see the crew come on deck, for none of the boys was more than seventeen years of age.

Ted wasn't particular about jobs when he returned to Edmonton, and when he started with the city didn't even bother to inquire about pay. He got $86 on his first bi-monthly cheque. From that, 65 cents was deducted for income tax, $2.02 for sick benefits, $3.41 for pension, plus a few other miscellaneous deductions. Although it wasn't a great sum of money, the percentage removed for income tax was certainly more attractive than the amount removed today.

Roy McBurney had been in Burma and India during the war. For some time after returning he must have thought he was still there, as he would ride his bicycle to work in -45°F comfort. He finally realized he was in Canada when he noticed icicles hanging from his face.

Roy was badly shaken by an incident that happened soon after he started. The telephone department had received a brand new truck which was the pride of the fleet. One day Roy smashed his glasses and his foreman loaned him the truck to drive home and pick up a spare pair. On the way back, Roy hit a patch of ice and smashed into the hind end of another car. He reported the accident, then lived in fear of being dismissed by Christie. Roy kept his job, but had to pay damages of $21.47, which was a sizable amount from a $90 pay cheque.

Ross McCutcheon started out on the test desk, moved into PBX troubleshooting and became an installation foreman. Ross was the repair shop supervisor when he retired in '78. Ross is known for his dry sense of humor which, once kindled, can keep a person in stitches for hours.

Alf Issacs was stationed in England during the war. After being discharged he went back to his job at AGT for a short time before he joined the city. Alf spent most of his telephone days in repair and he knew that department inside and out. Alf retired in '78, moving to British Columbia where he hoped to spend some of his time shooting wildlife with a camera.

Ken Sherwin was in the armored tank core in the army. He started out with CTS switching in Churchill Square. Now he's boundary cutover co-ordinator in the plant and central office department. Ken is a gourmet cook and has won prizes for his Parkerhouse rolls year after year at the annual Klondike Days home baking event.

Charles Wales started in '47 as a lineman, and later was in charge of the heavy gang. H. (Bud) Bradley retired in '78 as an inspector installer. Bud is quite an artisan; he does lathe metal work and has created many unique pieces.

Cec Rotto and Graham Barker came in '47. Graham Barker was in the air force during the war. After that he spent two years at the University of Alberta taking engineering. He came to CTS in '47 as an apprentice switchman, became a senior switchman, took over as chief switchman when Ben Davison retired, and moved into the engineering branch in the mid-sixties. Graham was a founding member of the South Side Athletic Club and volunteered some time to little league hockey.

George Evans started the next year. He's now a supervisor in construction and commonly called the "grouch" because he is anything but a grouch. Harvey Crawford, a decorated fighter pilot during the war, also joined the ranks. Albert Mills, Doug Kruse, Terry Tourigny and Sid Scheie are all still working with the department. Bob Anderson started as a cable splicer's helper. He had been working for some time before his foreman noticed that something was not quite right. The color-coded wires in the cable didn't match. It was then discovered that Bob was colorblind, whereupon he was transferred to the heavy gang.

Gordon Speers was another '47 rookie. There is a tale told of Speers which can compete with the best of Belanger. One night after Speers and Crawford had spent a few hours relaxing in a local beverage room, they proceeded to drive home but were having a great deal of difficulty getting the truck to move. Speers commented that the truck was pulling hard and it was no wonder; the following morning as construction barricades were removed from a downtown street, early morning travellers gazed upon a beautiful set of tire tracks in the day-old cement.

Forty-nine brought another group of new employees, the most that telephones had hired in a single year up to that point.

Newt Graham was a member of the signal corp during the war and was in the last signal unit to leave Germany. Newt had been working up north and stopped to visit friends in Edmonton on his way to his new job in Winnipeg with Manitoba Telephones. Edmonton caught his heart and he decided to stay. Newt is probably the only one in city telephones to have found a car in his office one morning. Apparently the man driving the vehicle the night before had taken a wrong turn and ended up smashing through a wall in the telephone building.

Roger Lejambe had been in the Second World War and the Korean war, coming back to telephones after both tours of duty. John Karchut had been a sergeant major in the army. His career started out on a sour note. He arrived at camp in Aldershot, England, only to spend the rest of the first day in jail. The new lads were pretty grubby after getting off the boat and there was no time to clean them up before the king was to arrive to do an inspection, so they were just put out of sight in the lock-up.

John Heck and George Whiteside were army boys. John, now a line foreman, is an executive officer in the Union and is also a member of the Alberta Umpires Association.

J. (Doug) Daugherty, C. (Les) Young, Lloyd Jennings, Mike Boon and Ray Forrest are also still with the department.

Myron Solojuk started out as a switchman and is now in the plant extension department as an engineering supervisor in charge of planning. Myron is also involved in the Millwoods transponder test.

Al Forbes also started off as a switchman and is now director of repair in the plant department. Al was one of the lucky ones who had friends working for telephones before he joined. He was warned about the initiation of new employees, and he managed to escape.

Al did get caught by one of Wilf Kinney's pranks. Wilf had an abstract manner about him that could catch a person off guard. Once, in order to determine who to send to the test desk, he asked if anyone could ride a motorcycle. Al said he could and Kinney told him to report to the test desk Monday morning. Al still can't figure out what riding a motorcycle had to do with working the test desk.

Stu Morrish, now in charge of wire centres, was known as the "Charles Atlas" of city telephones. Stu started as an apprentice switchman and worked his way up. He is quite adept at cabinet making and designing and building homes. Dick Woodward, of engineering, calls himself the sweetheart of city telephones because he was hired on Valentine's Day. Ray Goss also started as a switchman in '49 and is now customer equipment engineer. Ray is the man to talk to about new developments in station equipment.

Harry Rogers started in plant and six months later moved into engineering. That made a total of three in engineering in 1966. Harry was an air force war veteran and went to the University of Alberta, receiving his degree in electrical engineering before starting with city telephones. Harry is probably the most knowledgeable man around in technical information and historical methods.

Norville Robson's claim to fame, other than having a daughter who was the youngest female member (14) in the 1970 Canada Swim Team, is that he is a top-notch curler.

Gord Gerdes, another engineer, is an antique car lover. Gord is known as the fellow who sweet-talked a lady into selling him her mint condition 1917 Model T, and doing it after the antique car club had been beating down the lady's door with offers to buy.

Don Barry, a former Edmonton Eskimo and now coach of the University of Alberta Golden Bears, put some time in with CTS. Don started as an apprentice cable splicer and worked his way up to area engineering supervisor in outside plant engineering before transferring to the city's realty development office.

Bill Haydak, another forty-niner, is president of the local UFO society and a member of the Royal Astronomical Society. Bill built an eight-inch reflecting telescope and designed and built an equitorial mount. Bill is also a TV and radio expert and has been a ham radio operator for years.

The last few years of the forties could be remembered as the years that the telephone department constantly faced a barrage of irate customers waving telephone applications. Regularly each morning a number of citizens came in to discuss phone connections. The customer in the beginning usually just talked with a clerk. If he was unable to help, the zone clerk was called in. If he too admitted defeat, McCool was called in. It came to a point where all the customers were getting to see Christie.

Christie always tried to please the people, and this constant harassment and criticism took a lot out of him. Christie is remembered as a perfectionist, an honest man, tough but fair. Al Josey remembers one Christmas Eve in '47 or '48. He took an extra-long lunch break and came back around 3 PM a little bleary eyed to find Christie at his usual observation post behind the long counter in the Churchill Square office. Josey decided to take it like a man and told Christie he had been celebrating the season. Christie declared that Josey was the first man to tell the truth when caught doing something wrong. After that, Josey remembers, the rules were somewhat relaxed.

By the end of the decade, the department showed signs of making gains on the pile of applications. But citizens were warned that the battle could be won only if the orders scheduled to arrive in 1949 and 1950 came on time. Of the 8000 applications on file near the end of '49, some dated back to 1946. Outlying areas, such as Calder, had people that had been waiting since 1942. The phones were being installed as fast as possible but it wasn't fast enough to match the 15 to 20 new applications pouring into the office each day. The boys tried though, and betwen 1942 and 1949, 10,000 new phones were installed.

Another 2000 lines of equipment were ordered from Britain in '49, and by the end of the year city telephone officials were anticipating a saving of several thousand dollars if the English sterling exchange rates remained unchanged in 1950.

The Fifties and the Big Pinch

The fifties opened on a high note. The Edmonton telephone company had 8000 telephone applications on file. At the rate of 15,000 new applications a year, it was clear why the telephone department couldn't keep up to the booming Edmonton population. It seemed that every new family moving into the city wanted at least one telephone. Applications from babysitters and dressmakers requiring business phones in their homes were at an all-time high, and there was the consolation that even though Edmontonians may not have been well-connected telephonically, they were well-dressed and well-cared for.

Early in the decade a new fad appeared. Colored telephones were viewed as just that — a fad which would fade as quickly as it had come. In response to inquiries about colored phones, telephone spokesmen said that the City Telephone System (CTS) "refused to indulge in the fad of colored phones, not when it was impossible to keep up with demands for ordinary sets. "Experience proved," said chief Christie, "that people who demand a colored set installed want to exchange for another color every few months as their color schemes are changed."

By February of 1950, the waiting list was over 9000 but Edmonton was not alone in its misery. Calgary had 5000 applications on file, Winnipeg had 13,000 and B.C. Tel topped the list at 30,000.

In order to alleviate the phone problem, 125 more pay stations were scheduled for September installation. A person without his own telephone could run to the nearest pay station to make calls.

In November, council authorized the purchase of $164,950 worth of specialized phone equipment. The installation of 1100 lines in the west end was to give Edmonton one of the most modern automatic telephone exchanges on the continent.

By December, discontent with the phone situation was taking up a lot of time in council chambers. Alderman Innes was bothered, bewildered, but not bewitched. He suggested that an examination of city telephones be held because of the general dissatisfaction with present equipment. He felt that council should consider engaging a telephone consultant to report to council "on the technical efficiency of the apparatus and equipment of the telephone system according to approved modern standards, together with recommendations as to methods necessary to adopt in order to increase efficiency."

Experts had already studied the water system, transit system and the bridges. Two companies, Bell of Canada and Automatic Electric of Chicago, offered consulting services. Bell, in addition to inspecting and overhauling the system, would provide continuing supervision.

The system had a lot of problems, according to Innes. Because of a lack of interoffice trunk lines, telephones that weren't busy in one exchange would ring busy in another. Overloading was causing telephone users to route into the wrong circuits. The system didn't have a dial tone, and some of the obsolete equipment was causing "lock-up", which meant that when a number was dialled too quickly before hanging up for a sufficient length of time, the phone would appear to be dead since a complete disconnection hadn't been achieved. Another disgrace was the stack of phone applications dating back five and six years. Surely something could be done about that! Innes also wanted to know how many old phones were in use, and if the department was going to service an oil refinery and a roofing plant on the eastern outskirts of the city.

Superintendent Christie explained that these businesses had their own exchanges, therefore servicing them would not deprive Edmontonians of phone service. The city wasn't short of phones, he said, but of central office equipment.

As to the other allegations, Christie replied that the Edmonton system was one of the most modern and best-maintained systems in Canada. The difficulties were due to the shortage of equipment and the congestion of the system at peak load periods, which was a common problem. The dial tone would be coming in when long distance automatic toll dialling was made national. Alberta Government Telephones (AGT) was at the time installing a long distance automatic toll board and the dial tone equipment would be available at little cost, probably around April of 1951.

In reply to the question of interoffice trunking congestion, Christie said that exchange cable networks were installed in accordance with standard telephone practice, and all trunk circuits used larger-gauge wire between exchanges. The new telephones that were in use in Edmonton were some of the most efficient that could be purchased. There were no complaints from AGT regarding poor transmission out of Edmonton by toll users. Some overloading on lines, Christie admitted, was due to the policy of giving priority to business telephones. It was a situation which couldn't be completely rectified until more equipment was available so the load could be redistributed. The commissioners had decreed that business installations should be favored and cause some overloading rather than limiting the number of business telephones.

Complaints had steadily decreased over the previous 30 years, until in 1951 there were only 1.7 complaints per phone per year. The superintendent reminded the council that a phone also had to be treated properly. Much of the telephone trouble was caused by owner abuse. Christie also pointed out that no obsolete phone equipment was in use. The oldest equipment was 25 years of age, which was the same as the equipment being used in Saskatchewan and Manitoba Telephones. There were 8474 old-style telephones in use, but it was the policy of the department to replace these old phones only at the subscriber's request and at an extra cost of 25 cents a month in rental.

Christie and Innes were engaged in a battle of semantics as they obviously had different definitions for "obsolescence" and "inefficiency."

At the end of 1939 the city had 19,033 phones in use and by the end of 1950 it had 38,044 phones, a 100 percent increase over 11 years. That record was hardly shabby, considering that CTS had suffered from continual equipment shortages. Edmonton wasn't that badly off! Canada's total backlog numbered 100,000, and the United States was under an application pile of about one million.

At the end of 1950, 11,700 lines of automatic switching equipment were on order with specifications drawn up for 2000 more lines. About half was to be ready in 1951 and the remainder in early '52.

In January, the commissioners stated that phone rates should be raised, or the department would be in a serious financial position.

The proposed changes were to raise business phones $1.00 a month, and residential phones 50 cents a month. Installation fees would also go up $1.00. The private branch exchange trunk rate would go from $4.15 to $7.50. This rate increase was necessary since expenses had increased much faster than income.

Later that month, Christie asked council to accept his resignation as of March 8, his 65th birthday. He had intended to complete the year as superintendent but "an unwarranted reflection on my record of almost 50 years in the telephone business, among other things, has brought about a reconsideration of this decision."

Council said that the telephone investigations were in no way to be taken as a reflection on Christie's record, saying, "In our opinion, Mr. Christie is a most capable superintendent and during the past few years has had a most onerous job trying to allocate telephones fairly with such a backlog of applications to contend with." Christie was convinced to stay until the end of the year.

By May of '51, the telephone system was running out of five-digit numbers. Also in May, because of a paper shortage, the city decided that it would issue the phone book every eight instead of six months — a move which would alleviate pressure on the directory people.

By September, the backlog was down to around 7200, as the phone department had installed an average of 600 phones per month for the first 6 months and in July and August had installed 400, a decrease due to the inclement weather.

The dial tone was installed in the Edmonton system in October of '51. Also that year there was talk of Jasper Place and Beverly amalgamating with Edmonton. At the time, 225 persons in Jasper Place shared phones through 15 party lines. Edmonton didn't anticipate any difficulties with AGT regarding sale of the phone service in the area.

As 1951 reached a close, Superintendent Christie retired. Through the years he had kept up with changes and improvements in telephony. During the forties he established a library of tests and magazines for apprentices to contribute to their technical education. Even though most of his time was spent on the job, he had been a member of Empire Lodge Number 63 and of the Scottish Rite. He was also an active member of the Edmonton Lawn Bowling Club. But the long years he spent as telephone superintendent had taken their toll on Christie. In January of 1953, Robert Christie died at the age of 66.

Another "character" came to city telephones in 1951. Leo LeClerc started as an assistant zone clerk to Al Josey. He became a zone clerk then moved to yellow pages to give Ed Bolander, a long-time employee, a little help. Ed would be retiring soon and Leo was there to learn the ropes.

When Leo came, the yellow pages directory was losing about $90,000 per year. He took that department and changed it into a top-notch moneymaker for city telephones. Yellow pages became so well known that people weren't aware that Leo's yellow pages was actually a department of city telephones. It was so successful that in

1958, Paul Carroll of Bell took the phone book to the CANYPS conference as an example of a successful operation.

The first day on the job in yellow pages, Bolander gave Leo a phone book and a stack of contracts and told him to go and do his thing. Leo retired to the Royal George Hotel and over a cup of coffee wondered how he would tackle his responsibility. He was familiar with marketing procedures through his ten years in the hotel business. Leo was convinced there must be a way to make the yellow pages profitable, and he and his newly-hired salesman, Fred Windwick, proceeded to find the answers. "When in doubt, ask those who know," was Leo's motto, and to find out how the big telephone companies operated he and Fred would just have to visit them.

The backlog-plagued CTS department heads were not very attentive to Leo's inter-company visiting suggestion. Undaunted, Leo convinced Fred that they would have to do it alone, on their own time with money out of their own pockets. Loaded down with $300 cash and lots of enthusiasm and nerve, Leo and Fred puttered down to Seattle in Leo's Volkswagon. There they intended to visit Pacific Northwest Bell, one of AT&T's companies. They walked into the company's offices, confident and bold as brass, yet acknowledging Pacific Bell's leadership in the industry. They were well received and in the course of four or five days charmed the Americans into giving them armloads of information, including $50,000 worth of radio and TV ads.

When Fred and Leo returned they immediately wrote a report which included ideas for changes in the department. C. E. Brown, newly appointed superintendent, was so impressed that the company opened its purse and later sent the pair, all expenses paid, to study Mountain States Telephone and Telegraph in Denver, and to San Francisco to visit Pacific Telephone and Telegraph.

One of Leo's first changes was to remove the "hang-up hole" from the phone book, an item which had been obsolete for years. Also thanks to Leo, the telephone directory got dressed up in bright new clothes. In 1962, Leo suggested that a picture of the new city hall should be featured on the cover, instead of the usual ads. That started a tradition that has remained unbroken to this day. Recent covers have included tributes to the police and firemen of the city. A model of the Commonwealth Stadium dominated the phone book in 1978.

LeClerc stayed with city phones until 1966 when he started up the Business Development Department for the city. In 1975 he became Assistant Deputy Minister in Urban Transportation. He left the

Alberta government in the fall of 1978 to start his own consulting firm.

Part of Leo's fame has come from his association with hockey. In 1951 he got involved in organizing the Edmonton Oil Kings, and was general manager of the club from 1952 until 1965. He is a lifetime honorary director of Alberta Senior Hockey. He has moderated radio sports shows, was producer and host of a television panel show on CFRN in the sixties, and is currently hosting "LeClerc" again on CFRN. From '68 until '73 he was a panel member of CBC's quiz show. Leo has been made an honorary citizen of Texas, Montana, Nevada and the cities of New Orleans and Reno. He has received citations from the United Fund, Klondike Days Association and the Yellowhead Interprovincial Highway Association. He is a member and a past member of many clubs and associations.

Leo always found a way to reach his objectives, many times riding on nerve alone. When Fred and Leo were making their first out-of-country trip, they passed by a Nike Hercules Missile Base. At the time, the cold war was on everyone's mind. Leo was determined to see the base and drove up to the heavily-guarded gate despite protests from Fred.

"We're from Canada," began Leo, "and as Canadians, we're prepared to fight the next world war to the last drop of American blood. We just want to see the base and confirm that the Americans are doing a terrific job." They not only got past the gate, but received a guided tour as well.

Fred Windwick, Leo's partner in yellow pages, became advertising manager in '66 and directory manager in '67. He became marketing manager in '70, and general commercial manager in '71. In '77 he became general plant manager, which is the position he holds today.

Fred has been involved in a number of organizations including the Alberta Junior Football League. He has held almost every executive post in the Huskie Athletic Association and the Kinsmen Club of Edmonton. He has been involved in the Chamber of Commerce and the United Way, the Banff School of Advanced Management, and the Alberta School of Economic, Science and Social Philosophy. He is a member of the advisory board of the International Association for Students of Economics and Commerce.

Upon Christie's resignation at the end of 1951, Clarence E. (Buster) Brown, chief plant engineer, was appointed superintendent. Brown had been with the department for thirty-four years and was generally accepted as one of the most telephonically knowledgeable men ever to work for city telephones.

Brown started with CTS at the age of fifteen. In a matter of years he knew the utility inside and out, and from every angle. He knew what it was like to be a worker and what it was like to be an executive. He gained valuable experience as an officer in the IBEW union in the twenties.

Brown, at the age of forty-nine was presented with a 1952 New Year's present — a huge backlog of orders and a horde of impatient citizens who expected him to wave a magic wand and give everyone a telephone. Brown acknowledged that he was taking over a big job and credited Mr. Christie with "shouldering a difficult task successfully during the post war period of heavy demand and material and equipment shortages."

Brown was already well known in city and provincial sports circles. During and after his school days he played hockey, British rugby, soccer and basketball. He also coached boys' hockey. Brown was a president of the Alberta Fish and Game Association and a life member and director of the Edmonton Gun Club. Now retired, he maintains a lively interest in sports, trap and skeet shooting and hunting upland game birds.

In January of '52, the rate raises which had been suggested the year before were put into effect. Originally a $1 increase for businesses and a 50 cent increase for residences had been proposed, but at the suggestion of Alderman Miller, the rates were changed to $1.50 and 25 cents. This put business phones at $6.75 and $7 and residential phones at $3 and $3.25. By March, the department caught up with its 1950 backlog, reducing the applications on file to 6000.

By May, telephones were being installed at such a rate, and changes were being made so fast, that the telephone department had exhausted its supply of telephone directories. With five hundred changes and installations per month, telephone books were scarce. After that month, new telephone installations did not get a directory. Because of that turn of events, the information operators had an extra load to carry.

Although problems were slowly being overcome, complaints were still heard from the public about favoritism and inefficiency within the department. Installation crews were constantly busy, and most men put in many hours of overtime each week. One of the installers had attempted to get a phone in '51 when his wife was pregnant. He even got a doctor's note but couldn't get a phone installed. Citing his own case, he tried to tell subscribers that employees of the department didn't receive special treatment. They never believed him, so he gave up, but it got tiresome to be met at the door with, "Well, it's about time!" At this time there was a lot of hard feeling directed at the telephone company, and those employees who met the public took the brunt of the criticism.

In June another problem surfaced. Edmonton teenagers discovered a new game which city officials named "yell-a-phone." The dial tone on the south side was so soft that a person could take the receiver off the hook, yell into the phone and be heard above the tone. Without dialling teenagers could, according to one official, "exchange numbers, names and nonsense." This trick worked because the dial tone on the phone system was provided by a common line. A person was connected to the line when he lifted the receiver, and would be disconnected from it once he began dialling. The game worked only on the south side because the dial tone had been softened, at the subscribers' request. Once the game was discovered, the tone was quickly raised again, putting an end to the fun.

In September, contracts totalling $143,484 were awarded for constructing a new telephone exchange in the Idylwylde subdivision. Here council bent the rules a bit, awarding the contracts in one fiscal year, but not entering the amount until the next. It was necessary as the equipment for the new exchange, costing $235,155 would be arriving in the spring and there had to be a building to house it.

In '53, the population of Edmonton was 170,000. The total number of telephones had reached a figure of 53,470, about one phone for every three people. Edmontonians were a talkative lot that year, as the average number of calls per person was 944, or 3000 calls for each instrument. The March '53 directory grew by 148 pages, making a total of 1566. The directory brought out in October added a new feature. The 1800 AGT subscribers in Jasper Place were listed.

During the summer of '53, Edmontonians were made aware (if they weren't already) of the pitfalls of modern technology. The danger was invasion of privacy from the telephone. At the time there were many people using recording devices on their phones, such as legal offices, stores taking orders, and other parties who used a recording device instead of taking notes. In July, city council adopted a regulation which stated that all persons wishing to use a recorder in connection with their telephones had to have a warning device connected by the telephone system. The warning device would give a short beep tone every fifteen seconds, to inform the party on the line that he was being recorded. The warning device would go into operation as soon as the recorder was switched on. The city regulations also gave the telephone company authority to discontinue services to any person found using the recording devices over the phone without implementing the warning device.

In September, tenders were called by the city commissioners for construction of a new telephone exchange at 131 Street and 115 Avenue. The exchange was almost identical to the Idylwylde exchange. The project, including equipment, was to cost $375,000. Westmount Shopping Centre was just in the planning stages, and the telephone company planned to serve this proposed multi-million dollar shopping centre, the first in Edmonton, with the new Woodcroft exchange.

By December, the Idylwylde exchange was operating with 200 lines and another 4000 expected to be connected within a year. These lines wouldn't last long, since at the rate the city was growing there would be a phone waiting list of 8000 people by the end of '54. The problems just never seemed to end.

The management of the department and the installation crews weren't the only members of the telephone department with problems. The information operators were again feeling harassed. At peak time during the day "113", or information, was swamped with calls. In the fifties, the operators were seldom asked "How do you make a pie?", but they were repeatedly asked for numbers that were already listed in the directory. The problem was so acute that Minnie Tebbutt, chief operator, remarked, "Why bother printing a directory. Give me a few more operators and we'll handle the few extra calls."

There were then six information operators on duty at one time. Each one had a two-tiered circular card index in front of her which contained the 50,000 numbers in the city. These indexes were kept up to date by the day, and almost as soon as a new number was issued, it was up on the indexes. Already overworked on a normal day, the girls just dreaded the days that conventioneers flocked to the city and wished to call old friends, businesses, and new friends. Other bad times were the stormy days, for instead of going out and about, most business and socializing was done by telephone. It was much easier to dial "113" and get a number than it was to look in the book.

By October of '53 the city was planning to annex the town of Beverly. Plans were to start installing cables and instruments by early spring. There were already about eight subscribers in Beverly on the Edmonton system, with another 150 on the Edmonton rural system. A new exchange would not have to be built there, since at most 600 new subscribers would come from the area, and the city's north exchange could serve them quite well. The waiting list in the north end of the city was small and expected to be non-existent by spring. The same priorities in getting phones would apply to Beverly residents. The monthly rate of $2.25 for party-line service in the city would be increased by 75 cents which would cover the cost of out-of-city maintenance.

In the beginning of '54, the telephone department was reorganized. In December of '53, a number of long term employees — Jim McCool, assistant superintendent; George Kirkwood, plant chief; Cliff Butterworth, chief tester; and Tommy Rae, branch exchange foreman — had retired. With McCool's retirement, the department eliminated the position of assistant superintendent,   the last city department to do so. Wilfred Kinney was appointed the supervisor of commercial practices. With the shuffle, the telephone department was divided into two major groups — Mr. Kinney, as chief plant engineer, was in charge of buildings and equipment; Bert Billingsley was in charge of personnel and commercial activities, which included accounting, sales and the yellow pages and directory.

Bert Billingsley was a hard working, conscientious man who loved order. He made sure everyone knew what was going on by distributing countless interoffice memos. One of Bert's first memos gave the employees firm guidelines in dealing with persons demanding a phone. If the applicant stated that he needed a phone for business reasons, he must have a letter from business firms; if the applicant had a medical reason, a letter from a doctor would have to be sent to the department. For a change of number a subscriber would have to submit a written request, and a business request would have to be signed by the manager of the firm. Installers would henceforth collect one month's rent when the phone was installed, failing that the subscriber would be told that payment would have to be made within five days.

The Woodcroft telephone exchange opened in February of '55 with 150 lines operating and 1000 more to be added the following month. That was exchange number 6, and covered the area north of 109th Avenue and west of 124 Street. The numbers in the Woodcroft exchange had six digits.

New applications were being received at a rate of 800 per month, with 500 phones becoming available each month because of subscribers leaving the city. The department could not foresee any decrease in the backlog unless delivery of ordered equipment could be speeded up. Almost two years were required to manufacture and ship equipment once an order was placed. An alternative would be for city planners and builders to plan two years in advance of construction, leaving the telephone department some time to order equipment to serve the new areas.

In '55 the department decided to save some time, money and effort by issuing a directory once every year instead of every eight months. The estimated savings were about $95,000. The format would change from a three to a four-column page.

The waiting list was now about 5000. Although the list was getting smaller, the residents' complaints were getting louder. One book a year wasn't enough, they said. There would be so many changes in the numbers that by the end of the year the telephone directory would be absolutely useless. Go an entire year without updates — out of the question! If it had to be just once a year, then at least publish a supplement, citizens argued. Again there were accusations of favoritism and inefficiency. Council started calling for an inquiry into the telephone shortage. Again Brown had to point out that since it took two years to receive the equipment, and that equipment couldn't be ordered until the planning department knew which subdivisions would be opening next, there wasn't much the department could do. The twenty-six information operators on duty from 8 AM until 11 PM were also attacked. They were termed "inefficient." Because the demands of the job were so great, information operators didn't stay long. Most of them had less than one year's experience. Shift work, it was said, didn't appeal to most women. Many would take the job of city information operator only long enough to get enough experience to work for a private company. Another problem was the fast growing city, and the operators' unfamiliarity with the streets and addresses.

The department did get a few kind remarks when it introduced telephones colored in ivory, blue, red, rose and green. The only drawback was that these colored phones all had black handsets.

By February of '56 the waiting list had grown to 6000 and telephone facilities and services were under study by the community affairs committee of the Edmonton Chamber of Commerce. The committee concluded that there weren't enough phones on hand and that the future needs of telephone exchanges weren't provided for — hardly news to anyone! The committee recommended that after-hours business phones be checked for authenticity, as many people were still using this as an excuse to get residential phones. Another suggestion was to print emergency numbers on the inside cover of the directory, instead of on the first page which was often torn out.

The committee suggested that more pay stations be installed in the downtown area. The problem, however, was not only difficulty in finding equipment, but a lack of suitable sites for paystations. Brown felt that paystations would be damaged if located along city curbs. He suggested putting them alongside buildings, but this was turned down by the building owners. Paystations at the time were all inside business premises and the proprietors received commissions for them. There were also technical problems involved in operating phones outdoors. The cold Edmonton winters not only froze fingers and toes, but froze the lubrication in the instruments. It would be extremely frustrating for a cold person to have a paystation coin box gobble up his last dime, then refuse to work. The downtown pay station problem was shelved, but not before the council got a chance to hike the rate from a nickel to a dime. To serve some of the residential areas waiting for phones, plans were made to have outside booths installed in November.

By early '57, council was seriously considering offering party lines to subscribers in the city. This would allow more people to have a phone, if they didn't mind a little listening in. Brown was against the practice, sure that it would impair the department's public relations. But town council over-ruled him and began publicizing the fact that persons in congested areas might obtain a telephone sooner if they could find neighbors with telephones who would agree to a temporary party line. Many people took advantage of this service and a number of two-party lines were established.

A few light moments in telephone history received publicity. One event occurred in August of '56. The drama started when a citizen attempted to make a prearranged call to the barrister's office in the city police station. The number was dialled, it rang endlessly, but no one answered. The barrister then phoned the person in the police station, and it was discovered that the number in the book didn't match the number of the telephone on the desk. The phone department was called in and a repairman was sent to the scene. The repairman quickly located a line and traced it to the second floor. The barrister's office had a phone with a different number which was also listed in the directory. At this point a reporter joined in the quest for the phone. Each installation in the building was checked, including Magistrate Dupre's office where the judge joined in the search. Chief Anthony and other officials were called in on the case but no clues could be found. The repairman checked the box again, declaring the phone was somewhere in the building. A further check was fruitless and the phone man went away baffled, as did the criminal minds in the police station. The case remained unsolved, however it was later learned that in '54 the phone had been replaced by another, and the original listing, through some oversight, remained in the directory.

By November there were 80,000 phones in service and applications were coming in at the rate of 1000 per month. Brown was literally begging for more equipment in order to keep reasonably close to the backlog. He foresaw an expenditure of $2,500,000 to include warehousing and storage space, lines of central office equipment, and a needed extension to the Idylwylde exchange, plus cables of all sizes.

Council was beginning to accept the idea of keeping more equipment in stock, as they could see that it was the only way to solve the problem of backlogs. Brown also suggested that builders should wire homes for phones during construction, as they did with electrical service.

Again, a very strict priority system was established. First to be served were business applications, then medical needs, then aged persons living alone, residence telephones for management in special services of police, and fire and security personnel. At the bottom of the list were residence applications, in order of the date of application.

One problem of '57 was the large number of people who dialled the street address instead of the telephone number. This was quite a bother, for if the first three letters dialled were 100 or 114, the caller was immediately put in touch with the fire, police and ambulance service.

By May of '58 contracts of $360,000 were awarded for additions to the Idylwylde exchange and the main exchange. The main exchange was to get a partial two-storey addition and an extension.

That year the department started planning for the two-letter, five-digit number dialling system which was to be inaugurated in 1959. Of the 93,000 phones in use in the city, the dial plates on 5000 phones were obsolete, as they showed only numbers. These phones were slowly replaced and number changes were instituted on the south side.

The phone department was averaging 1000 installations per month and had chopped the waiting list down to 3000. Mr. and Mrs. E. Robertson became Edmonton's one-hundred-thousandth customers later that summer. A white desk phone bearing that inscription sat in the Robertson's home for a month. It was replaced with a regular phone and the white phone was removed to the city archives.

Citizens had a greater variety of phones to choose from that year. New one-piece instruments in six different colors were imported from Sweden. The swan-necked instruments were first offered as extensions, with plans to use them as first phone sets if they proved efficient. This particular phone had the dial face under the base of the instrument. Just lifting the phone off the desk could release the button connecting the call to central. The weight of the phone disconnected the line when it was set down on the desk.

In December the city telephone department opened new warehouse quarters by 107 Street and 121 Avenue. The move to the service centre enabled comptrollers to take stock, and a card stock control system was set up.

Late that year the Trans-Canada Telephone System assigned names to Edmonton exchanges in preparation for the two-letter, five-digit dialling plan which was to be instituted in early '59. The old main exchange became GArden, the south side became GEneva, Woodcroft exchange became GLendale, the north side exchange was GRanite, Idylwylde became HOmestead, the west end was HUnter, and Jasper Place was HUdson. The government buildings would be CApital, Sherwood Park was OXford and Namao was SWift. All prefixes in Edmonton had to begin with G, H, or I, which were all number "4" on the dial. Telephone officials were unhappy with the names, stating that only one, CApital, had any meaning. The others had no association with the areas.

When the '59 phone book came out, the new exchanges were listed by their new names. Another change made was in deleting listings for the surrounding towns and villages. The rural numbers were carried instead in a northern district directory put out by AGT. Rural telephone subscribers would have to pay an extra dollar to receive a city telephone book. The directory still had listings for Jasper Place, Beverly and St. Albert.

By the early part of '59, Edmonton boasted one phone for every 2.5 people. The backlog pile held 2950 applications, but the situation was improving. City telephones had enough equipment, it was announced, to fill all waiting orders for service within the corporate limits of Edmonton. The longest estimated waiting period should not exceed six months, and that included Beverly. If that was the case then maybe, just maybe, CTS would ride into the sixties with a clean slate.

The cutover to the two-letter, five-digit system of dialling was scheduled for March 15 and officials were hoping it would be a nice day, for if it was blustery and cold everyone would stay indoors and visit over the phone, clogging the lines.

Officials were apprehensive. After a year of educating the public as to the change, would all the people, especially the elderly, be aware of the changeover? Had all the obsolete phones been replaced? The telephone department did not have any records as to the number and location of the old phones.

The changeover was technically smooth, but the department was surprised at the great number of people who weren't aware of the changeover.

The information operators had two changes to contend with — the two-letter five-digit system and the change to a special book for looking up numbers, rather than cards rotating in turrets. The books were recommended for systems having over 100,000 phones. To keep up with changes, addendums were printed daily.

In the spring, preparations were made for the installation of the emergency call box system. Equipment valued at more than $50,000 was acquired, including a 400-line switchboard costing $35,000 to be located in the Edmonton Fire Department's communications centre. Officials announced that eventually each of the 400 lines would have a corresponding alarm box. All lines would be completely supervised and it would be impossible for a box to be disconnected without being immediately observed.

The boxes would be located, like the existing fire alarm boxes, on lamp posts or individual pedestals. In this system, callers were immediately connected with an operator at the fire control centre when the caller removed the receiver from the hook.

Installation of 100 boxes in the downtown area was scheduled for the end of April. When the alarm boxes began operation, Edmonton joined a select company of only two other Canadian cities with similar systems. The call boxes would be used for fire, police or ambulance. It was said that Edmonton was the only system in the nation to enable citizens to call any emergency service. The other two cities had only police and fire on their systems.

In December, J. B. (Bud) McCaulay was named to the newly established post of administrative supervisor of the city telephone system. McCaulay was responsible to the phone superintendent for administrative and financial matters.

Despite the rush, the overtime, and the complaints, the fifties provided its share of frivolity. Initiation was still a popular sport and supplier's employees were invited to play. Employees were merciless when it came to industry rookies. Ben Davison once stumbled upon a newcomer dressed in rubber hat, rubber apron, rubber goggles, gloves and boots, holding a pail beneath a cut cable. When asked what he was doing, the fellow replied in all seriousness, "catching voltage drop." The plant men were behind that caper.

One of the department's long-running wars started during this period — the infamous series of battles between Ted Bennett and Leo LeClerc. Although the origin of the war is long forgotten, the incidents will live on in telephone history annals.

Bennett, described by one of his workmates as a big lovable bear, could easily be goaded into nonsense and LeClerc needed no prompting at all. LeClerc was usually the instigator, but sometimes to brighten a day, a fellow employee might whisper to Ted, "Hey, Leo's talking about you," and Bennett would set after a surprised and innocent LeClerc. Many times the wiley LeClerc would be caught and suffer a few bumps and bruises. On one occasion LeClerc sought refuge in the lavatory but Bennett caught him and proceeded to flush him down the pipes. Only LeClerc's ability to hold his breath saved him from drowning.

Sometimes Leo and Joe McLafferty would team up and devise "get Ted schemes." Once Joe attacked Ted with an invisible ink pen. It's said that Ted chased Joe through the exchange and through the AGT toll building before realizing he had been the victim of a harmless prank.

Another successful "get Ted scheme" was to offer everyone in the lunch room a stick of gum, everyone except Ted that is. When Bennett finally demanded his share, he was given a stick which had been picked up (expressly for that purpose) some time earlier at the Magic Shop by Fred Windwick. In a few chews Ted would make a mad dash to the nearest watering hole to put out the fire in his mouth.

Ted would stop quite regularly at the Queen City Meat Market after work. One day Windwick and LeClerc ambushed Bennett as he came out of the store, Fred punching the meat out of Ted's arm into the waiting hands of LeClerc who bounded at top speed down the street past stunned onlookers with Bennett burning up the sidewalk in pursuit.

Windwick had his day. On one occasion the men all decided to wear bow ties instead of ties to work. Fred refused to comply (some say Leo put him up to it) and came to work sporting a new tie, which was immediately cut off by Bennett. Fred did get his revenge years later at Ted's retirement party. After practising for years, Fred wielded the scissors and neatly snipped Ted's tie in two.

Another popular victim in the fifties was Stu Morrish. Early in the decade, Stu bought a brand new Harley Davidson. That bike was Stu's pride and joy, and he'd usually park it at the service station beside the Churchill exchange in full view of his window. One day

McLafferty decided to have some fun with Morrish. Disguised in a raincoat and cap he skulked around the bike. Stu saw the suspicious-looking character lurking around his bike and he sped downstairs to investigate, but when he got outside the man had disappeared. A few minutes later Stu glanced out the window and saw the scoundrel sitting on his bike. Down the stairs Stu raced, four steps at a time, but again the fellow had disappeared. Some time later Stu again looked out the window to check on his bike. Low and behold the villain was bouncing up and down on the bike, looking for all the world like he and it would soon disappear. Stu flew down the stairs, dashed into the parking lot and pulled the thief off the bike before he could escape. About to give him a good shot in the head, he peered into the laughing eyes of a fellow employee and turned to see a row of snickering people watching the drama from the exchange windows.

A lot of people came to CTS in the fifties, and it looked as if Churchill Square would burst at the seams. Two new faces were George Chilton, who had been prisoner of war in Crete during the Second World War, and Rod Small, a bagpipe-playing naturalist. Roland Aicher came in '50 and brought with him eight years experience from AGT and thirteen from rural telephone systems. Roland spent most of his twenty years at City Telephones in charge of city pay phones. Gus Graham and Jim Butchart of engineering came in '50, as did Milt Candler, antique car buff, and Eugene Brenda. Brenda has thrilled Edmonton and Alberta audiences through the years with his daredevil skiing. He won the Alberta Ski Jumping Championship and the Classy Camrose meet. Gene currently represents the Northern Alberta Telephone Pioneers on the Alberta Rehabilitation Council. Percy Coggles came to city telephones as the first official painter in the paint shop.

In 1951 Al Crowell, Ray Schafer, Bill Hodgson and Orville Burchby joined engineering and Ed Gross joined the plant staff. Ed Bakalech of central office came in '52, and the following year brought John Roberts and Dave Winitoy of plant. Jim Campbell and Ken Laubman of customer services engineering came in '54, as did Nick Yaseko of central office. Tru Perry came that year. He is an amateur radio operator and has logged calls to over 295 countries.

Ken Bristow joined the repair shop in '55 and Gord Evans came to plant distribution. Chief operator Nellie Anquist came in '55 as did Jack Horley, the telephone department representative for the Northern Alberta Telephone Pioneers. Then 1956 came, bringing with it Stan Lucky of engineering, Peter Butler of the radio shop, Dick Ashmore of plant staff and Bernie Winters of plant.

Brian Airth came in '56. Brian is a master shooter. He was Centre Fire Open Champ in '65, the Canadian Champ in '66 and one of five men representing Alberta at the winter games in Quebec in 1967.

Engineering's Al Perry and Plant's George Mitchell came in '57. Nelson Modin of engineering came in '58 and Rick Vanderlinden of engineering arrived in '59. Information operators Isabelle Peters came in '55, Aulie Pasula in '57, and Sophie Richardson and Shirley McInnes (group chief operator) came in '59.

The fifties were tumultuous and fast-paced years for the telephone department. They were years of tremendous change and rapid growth for the department. Despite much criticism, by the end of the decade the telephone system was technologically improved. There were also different colors and styles of phones available. A number of new exchanges had been built and old ones expanded. The staff had grown appreciably and the list of subscribers jumped from 36,000 in '49 to 114,000 in '59. The list of applications on hand had dropped from 8000 to 1500, and Edmonton was in touch with cities all across Canada with the new two-letter five-digit dialling system. It seemed that the twenty years of large backlogs and long delays were finally over.

'et' Comes of Age

The change to two-letter, five-digit dialling was only nine months old when Superintendent Brown told the city of some tests Bell had been doing. Bell was conducting a seven-digit dialling study on two American exchanges. The results showed that less confusion resulted in using seven digits and it gave the exchanges more numbers to choose from. Alberta Government Telephones (AGT) had been watching the test and was considering seven-digit dialling for the province. Brown expected the city to change within four years.

A "plug-out" by-law passed in January startled a few citizens. A total of 22 city subscribers were disconnected because they didn't pay their long distance bills. The by-law did its job. In one week over one thousand overdue accounts were paid.

In anticipation of amalgamation with Beverly, the telephone department started building an underground ductline for telephone cables to that area.

By April, the city was seriously considering a raise in telephone rates. Edmonton rates were $3.25 per month for residential phones and $7.00 for business phones. Rates in comparable eastern Canadian cities were quoted as being $4.75 to $5 for residential phones and $12 to $14 for business phones. The telephone surplus for 1960 was expected to be only $320,000 and if Edmonton was going to pay for the change to direct distance dialling, it would have to come up with more cash. A fully-automated direct distance dialling system was expected to cost around $1.5 million, and a semi-automatic system would cost several hundred thousand dollars.

In May, 94 emergency call boxes were put into operation downtown, at major intersections and on arterial roads. The $100,000 system not only included calls for the police, fire departments and ambulances, but calls to report fallen power lines and other emergencies. The telephone department expected that gas and electric light trouble calls would be included later. When completed, the city-wide system would have 400 emergency call boxes. The bright red color and the words "Emergency", "Fire" and "Police" printed on the boxes would ensure that the phones were visible to the public.

The new plastic age had its drawbacks, some subscribers learned. A woman couldn't answer her phone if it rang while she was baking or applying makeup, because the new colored telephones were made of a very soft plastic that easily absorbed oils and chemicals. If a woman didn't wash her hands before picking up the phone, she might end up with a blotchy set and a fine for damaging the instrument.

The city was spilling into the fields surrounding its limits and new facilities were planned to service all the new subscribers. In December, tenders were let for a new telephone exchange to be built at 60 Avenue and 114 Street. The Trans-Canada Telephone System assigned the name "Hemlock" to the new exchange in the Grandview Heights subdivision. The total cost of the Hemlock exchange was to be about $200,000.

The department had caught up with telephone demand by the sixties but there were still complaints of inefficient service. A study made on the system in '61 showed that 24,000 trouble calls were reported, a substantial increase over the 1960 total of about 14,000 calls. The department blamed the increase in trouble calls on plain bad weather and the fact that many more subscribers were tied into the system. The people weren't going to be that easily pacified though, and reminded the phone officials that the list of subscribers hadn't doubled but the trouble calls had. The fact that City Telephone System (CTS) had sixty information operators was disturbing to some who claimed that other cities the same size as Edmonton didn't have that many operators.

As a chorus of voices joined to complain, another rose to defend. City telephones got an "A+" when it came to directories. Edmonton had one of the most accurate directories on the continent, averaging only one-tenth the number of mistakes set by the Bell companies as the maximum allowable before officials got nervous. Bell's figure was 3 per 1000 listings, CTS averaged 3 per 10,000 listings.

In 1961 more phone styles became available. CTS was offering colored night light phones, available in the princess or starlight models. Later that year, spacemaster telephones became available in ivory, white, beige and yellow. Spacemaster phones were wall and desk mounted compact models with the dial positioned on a swivel on top of the phone.

In 1962 Edmontonians could get code-a-phones with a beep tone and one 60-minute tape. Extension chimes and 880 loudspeaker telephones could be had for a few dollars more. Also that year, the new prefixes 429, 482 and 434 joined the CTS family and the Caravan Motor Hotel led Alberta hotels in the installation of a direct dial telephone system. A meter system was also installed to ensure proper payment of the guests' calls.

A number of AGT area subscribers became part of the local directory. St. Albert, Sherwood Park, Jasper Place, Ellerslie and Edmonton rurals, the International Airport and Namao residents were listed. The statistics at the end of the year showed that Edmonton residents made an average of 1,000,000 calls per day, again proving that they were a talkative lot.

In 1963 Edmonton followed the lead of larger North American systems and began to change to seven-digit dialling. Half of the entries in the year's directory were seven-digit numbers. The remainder of the city was to be changed in '64. Another change in the directory was the many names that were conspicuous by their absence. According to CTS administrative assistant, Bud McCaulay, so many people wanted silent numbers that the practice was reaching epidemic proportions. The telephone department had started the service to protect the city's well-known citizens from being harassed by crank callers and pests. Now ten percent of phone subscribers had silent numbers, a much higher percentage than other cities of comparable size, and McCauley believed that many people with silent numbers didn't need them.

One thing these people weren't bothered by was telephone soliciting. A few enterprising individuals, in an effort to attract advertisements to their proposed advertising book, were telling businesses that CTS was going out of the yellow page business and their firm would be taking it over. A person could advertise in this new book for $2.50 per month. The local Better Business Bureau and city hall personnel spent many hours reassuring citizens that yellow pages would remain a part of the city telephone directory.

Soon after, CTS started discussing rate increases. In an attempt to reduce the number of yellow pages in the directory and increase advertising revenue by about 15 percent, a rate increase of 58 percent was proposed. CTS assured businesses that this did not necessarily mean that they would have to pay more for their advertising, they could just cut down on the size of their ad.

One rate that was raised was the re-connection rate, bringing it to the amount charged by AGT. Persons wishing to re-connect phones which had been disconnected due to non-payment of accounts would have to pay $2 instead of the 50 cent fee that had been established in the thirties.

In '64, AGT started installing telephone equipment in the city in preparation for direct distance dialling, scheduled for 1966.

Yellow pages made news again in '65. It was expanding its circulation area to include businesses from Red Deer to Inuvik. The trade, development and commerce section of the Edmonton Chamber of Commerce arranged for 10,000 extra copies of the yellow pages to be printed. This was the result of two years of work by the trade, development and commerce committee whose members had visited 46 communities interviewing residents to discover what sort of problems they encountered trying to do business with Edmonton firms. CTS was to foot the printing bill and the Chamber of Commerce paid the distribution costs.

Another change instituted in '66 resulted in an even more compact directory. In July of '65 the decision was made to delete the pink pages, or the numerical listings of telephone numbers from the '66 phone book. The pages cost around $40,000 each year and the department felt this was an unnecessary expense, for the pink pages were not greatly used.

Near the end of '65, the city announced that upon the retirement of C. E. Brown at the end of the year, Stan Hampton of the city power department, would become the new superintendent of the telephone department.

Then it was back to school for a number of employees. Direct distance dialling (DDD) was coming and the staff would have to understand the new system, and how to operate and maintain it. CTS operators and plant personnel were receiving training on the new DDD system that AGT and CTS were jointly installing at a cost of $3,518,000.

Some of the operators learning to use the new system were Innes Ewald, Fran Kerr and Bernice Weissenberger, all veterans of '64. Florence Williams and Eleanor Rutherford joined the information department just in time to see the institution of DDD. Operators Rose Debuliak and Elfie McKeen were with the department at that time, as were Cathie Rocchio and Alice Vantour. Mary Van Larken started as an information operator and a few years later moved into repair. Mary Glenday was another employee who moved from information to repair. Bea Robertson started in '63 and stayed until '78. Bea, holder of a gold medal in ballroom dancing, has competed in western Canada and the northwestern United States. Velma Bogart is a communications administrator in directory assistance, Nellie Lipsey spent a number of years with the company in repair, and Jean Anderson, who started as an information operator in '65 is now with the Centralized Automated Loop Reporting System (CALRS) project, a computerized trouble report and detection system.

Not all the women who came in the sixties were in information and repair. Lil Whiteside started in '63 as a service advisor and is now a supervisor in that department, and Delores McPherson worked in the teletype section of traffic, and was teletype supervisor before moving to the plant staff department.

In 1966, the department started a service that proved very helpful for telephone users. When a subscriber moved, his old residential telephone number was placed on operator intercept for a period of thirty days, then on mechanical intercept. In the case of business moves, the old number was placed on operator intercept until the new directory came out. In the case of residential removals, the old number was placed on mechanical intercept.

That Christmas, a popular new gift made its appearance in many a Christmas stocking. An extension phone was a perfect gift for the teenager always on the phone, and for mom who could use an extension in her work area. Persons with extension phone gift certificates would have their new instrument connected immediately after the Christmas holiday.

As the last page of the '66 calendar was ripped off the wall, CTS was on the brink of a marvelous new advance in telephone technology. Touch tone phones would be arriving — 600 lines would be installed by the end of '67. Touch tone phones gave faster service and there was less chance for error by touching the wrong number.

In January CTS reached a new high in numbers of telephones — there were 175,000 instruments in the city. It was announced that the University of Alberta would receive Edmonton's first data transmission service. A special data phone hookup would connect most of the university's departments with the new IBM computer, which meant that information could be fed to the computer by phone, rather than having to make a special trip to the data room.

The telephone department was offering its customers closed circuit TV. There was talk of picture phones and electronic exchanges predicted to be in use in Edmonton by 1970, only three short years after Canada's first electronic exchange was to be installed at the 1967 exposition in Montreal.

In 1967, the telephone department changed its name to 'edmonton telephones' to fit its new look and new philosophy, and in March an 'et' house organ began publication. The "Communicator" was a vehicle for company and personal news for the system's 700 employees. The newsletter was not published on a strict schedule but as news was available, averaging four publications a year. Industry news was included as well as personal items such as marriages, births, promotions and other achievements. Different sections of the organization would be featured in different issues. Of course industry jokes were also included, like the following one. William Griep, applications clerk, tells of the man hired by the telephone company to collect money from pay phones. He didn't return to the office after his first work day. After two weeks his supervisor finally got him on the phone and asked him to come in and pick up his paycheck. Surprised, the fellow remarked, "You mean I get wages too?"

Don McAmmond from yellow pages was the magazine's first editor. He was followed by Phil Gordon and Wally Bazelewich. Phil Gordon, one-time city handball champ and a regular entrant at the Hawaiian Open, has been the editor since 1973. Jack Horley, Gene Brenda, Roy McBurney and Nick Shamley are contributing photographers. For some time 'et' artist John Barton did the layout, but now Phil does a rough sketch and leaves the rest to the printer.

In January of '67, Stan Hampton hired two new men to develop a marketing section for city telephones. Bryan Holmes and Al Bleiken were recruited from AGT.

Bryan had joined city telephones back in '49 as an office junior. It was his job then to collect money from the pay stations and deliver the mail. He joined AGT shortly after, staying with the company until moving to city telephones. In '69 Bryan was transferred to the directory section and presently is the manager of the section. Bryan has also been swimming coach at Jasper Place and Mill Creek pools and president of both clubs. He was on the founding committee of Sports Alberta and has held executive positions on provincial swimming organizations. His daughter Brenda, a world class swimmer, participated in the Munich Games in '72. Bryan was active in the '78 Commonwealth Games, as communications manager for the aquatic centre and commercial manager for the media.

While Bryan was setting up the marketing section, Al Bleiken was developing training programs for all phases of marketing. He had worked with AGT as a communications consultant and was training instructor for the marketing division of AGT in Edmonton. After organizing and developing the program, Al left 'et' in '75 to become manager of the city's business department.

Stan Hampton was made a city commissioner in the latter part of '67, leaving 'et' looking for a new leader. In August, Doug Burrows of Manitoba Telephones, was named new 'et' head to take over the department effective October 1.

Shortly after his takeover Doug Burrows announced that 'et' would begin an orderly process of retiring the step-by-step equipment in the exchanges and replacing it with the latest in electronic or electromagnetic equipment.

That year brought touch tone phones to Edmonton, the first to be installed in western Canada. Burrows intended to have touch tone phones installed in all pay telephone booths by March of '68, the same time that residential installations were to begin. Seven hundred phones were available in the GArden exchange for a basic rate of six dollars. The phones came in a choice of white, beige, blue or green. Edmontonians took to the touch tone phones, and 'et' reported a boom in paystation business for 1968.

Also in '67 a number of subscribers began requesting antique phones. At the time 'et' didn't have such phones available, but said that if subscribers wished to buy these phones from retail outlets and hook them into the city system, they would first have to be tested in the 'et' shops so that transmission and reception could be upgraded to 'et' standards.

By 1967 computers were the talk of the industry and general manager Burrows was looking ahead to the time when computers would replace information operators. The machine in the news was a computer that talked, developed by Bell research. (However it had problems with French, German and Ukrainian accents.) In this system, only two operators would be needed to answer incoming calls and plug them into the computer. The prototypes had been developed at the time but the high cost made widespread use impractical. After some study, this computer system was not found as practical as first anticipated, and 'et' later changed its information or "411" department to a computer data base with operators, which is the system presently in use.

At the end of the year, the phone department was planning a rate raise, from $3.75 to $4.25 a month for black residential wall phones, and from $10 to $11 a month for business phones. The rate increases were necessary as the money in the 'et' capital expansion fund for '68 was almost down to nickels and dimes. 'et' had made a profit of $2.5 million that year, but the money would go to reducing the city tax rate.

The new '68 telephone books took on a new look, much to the dismay of a number of people. The usual conservative cover was replaced by a collage of Klondike era pictures of lacy ladies and muscle-bound men. Many irate females used their new push button phones to call the department and inform it of their disapproval.

Then came concern over the abuse of the department's information service. Because people were not using the service properly, it cost a great deal of money and there was again talk of replacing the multitude of operators with computers. Most information calls were for numbers already listed in the directory. People calling information were being asked for their numbers and a record of calls was kept in an effort to identify who was making the unwarranted calls.

Another concern at the time was the large number of abusive and crank calls. About sixty complaints were received each month by the department, and of those about fifteen concerned abusive callers. The public was told that by 1972 'et' would have electronic equipment that could automatically trace and pinpoint these calls.

In November of '68, 'edmonton telephones' submitted an application to operate a cable TV system. By the end of the year Edmontonians topped the list of most talkative people in Canada. Again more calls per phone and per person were made in Edmonton than anywhere else in Canada.

That year, Paul Trawick, now general commercial manager, and Stan Shpiel, organization, development and financial results manager joined the staff of 'edmonton telephones'.

Paul Trawick began his telephone career in 1951 with Sask Tel, and achieved a responsible position in equipment and building engineering. He left in 1965 to join an Edmonton management consulting firm in telecommunications. Trawick joined 'et' as services manager to convert the telephone accounting system to the type of system used by the telephone industry, commonly called the uniform system of accounts. He then became general plant manager and in 1976 was made general commercial manager.

Trawick is an accomplished musician. He began piano lessons at the age of five and later switched to trumpet playing, becoming part of the Royal Sea Cadet Band in Saskatoon. He became musical director of that band. A few years ago Paul won the Dr. George Naylor award for displaying on a clarinet "the most rapid musical advancement and proficiency" at the Cosmopolitan Club award night banquet. Trawick was one of seventy persons answering an ad for adults who wanted to play a musical instrument or had played one as a child and wished to become a member of the Cosmo Club's adult band. He now plays clarinet for the Cosmo concert band and clarinet and saxaphone for a Dixieland Jazz Band.

Trawick was twice president of Cosmopolitan International of Edmonton, Governor of the Western Canada Federation of Cosmopolitan International and was on the board of the Cosmo music society. He is past-president of the Edmonton Chapter of Northern Council of the Telephone Pioneers of America, and is a governor of CITA (Canadian Independent Telephone Association).

Stan Shpiel joined the department to work with Trawick to organize a system of accounts to maintain uniformity of assets, liabilities and expenses. The preparation and implementation of this system kept Stan busy from the fall of '68 to the end of '69. Stan received his Bachelor of Commerce degree from Montana State University in 1965 and in 1976 became a Registered Industrial Accountant. Stan is very active in the department's telephone society, having held the positions of vice-president, president and past-president in addition to the post of treasurer which he has held for the past few years.

Bob McIntyre, now president of Capital Cable TV, joined 'et' in '68. He came to engineering to set up the plant extension department, and was involved in the early stages of the automatic meter reading studies and tests.

Three third level managerial people joined 'et' in the sixties — Ron Sollanych came in '66, Gordon Lambe in '68 and Ken Digweed in '69.

Ron Sollanych, now plant extension engineer, received his engineering degree from the University of Alberta, then went to work for Bell Canada in Montreal for a year before joining 'et.' Ron is interested in electronics and is involved in hockey in the northwest community clubs and the Alberta Amateur Hockey Association.

Gordon Lambe, now 'et' equipment and building engineer, joined as traffic engineering supervisor and two years later became the section's manager. Gord is a fisherman, hunter and skier, and an ex-member of the Alpine Club. Gord climbed for twenty-five years, during which time he climbed the second highest mountain in Alberta.

Ken Digweed, director of plant staff, joined 'et' in outside plant engineering. Ken took electronics technology at the Northern Alberta Institute of Technology (NAIT) prior to joining Bell Canada in Montreal. He was involved in the initial study into the CALRS project in '77. Ken belongs to the Shetland Sheep Dog Club, shows Shelties and teaches obedience training.

There were changes going on in the directory department in the second half of the sixties. Under Fred Windwick the department changed from an outdated galley system of production to a modern method. Paula Davis, now directory training officer, came to 'et' from the newspaper business. She worked many hours of overtime when the department was changing to the new system. Lil MacKenzie, white pages supervisor, and Peggy Armstrong, CANYPS (Canadian National Yellow Pages Service) co-ordinator, were also involved in the changeover.

At the beginning of '69, Edmontonians could dial "421-1111", and get the correct time. On March 9, Edmonton became the first city in Canada to institute the "911" emergency number that was becoming the universal help number all across North America. By dialling "911", the caller could immediately reach hospitals, police, fire stations and ambulances. The number provided fifteen emergency services, including gas and power trouble. The first official "911" call was placed by Mayor Ivor Dent and received by the city police Chief Constable Sloan.

It took the city a while to get used to "911" and exactly what it stood for. In the first week of operation, 1918 calls were received, and of these only 351 were true emergencies. Of the total, there were 485 calls from people who didn't respond, 333 wrong numbers, 100 routine administration calls, 111 calls for directory assistance, 72 for telephone repair, 21 crank calls, 36 from children playing with phones, 5 for the RCMP and 92 unassignable calls. There were 493 calls for police, 47 for fire, 84 for ambulances and 49 for hospitals. One woman called "911" when she won a television bingo and couldn't get through to the TV station.

Later that year, 'et' installed an AE-1 type PABX in the clinical sciences building on the University of Alberta campus; the first futuristic contempra phones arrived; and 'et' overhauled the trouble shooting system.

In the summer the city was talking about a proposed city run cable TV system that would bring American programs to Edmonton and provide low-cost TV phones. A city submission to the CRTC proposed that 'et' be given the right to operate a 10 million dollar community antenna TV system. The proposed rates were a $10 house installation fee and a $5 monthly rental for one TV and an extra $1 for additional sets. Bulk connections to apartment and office buildings would cost $2 each. It was proposed that the city of Edmonton should own the CATV system, to provide for financial integrity, sound community planning, efficient communications and financial equality for city residents.

On September 26, Judy Ann Bellovance became 'et's' two-hundred-thousandth phone customer. Mayor Dent and Superintendent Doug Burrows installed the phone. After one year, the gold plated touch button contempra, provided free of monthly charge, would be placed in the city archives. The phone was similar to the one in the Governor General's residence in Ottawa. On that note, 'et' entered the seventies.

Love is Better
the Second Time Around

During the 1960s the thirty-year truce between Alberta Government Telephones and the City Telephone System had come to an abrupt end, and once more tempers grew hot as rumors and speculations circulated.

The battle rekindled over a fairly innocuous comment. Alderman G. Prudham, at one of the first council meetings of the year, asked Superintendent Brown a question: from an engineering point of view, would it be advisable to have some integration between the City Telephone System (CTS) and AGT sometime in the future? Brown replied in the affirmative. He further stated that at some future point in time, it might be impractical for Edmonton to operate as a separate entity.

The next day the media jumped in. Was city telephones going to be absorbed by AGT? Mayor Roper was quick to say that Brown's statement was not to be taken as a suggestion of amalgamation. "Mr. Brown's opinion," said the mayor, "was given only on the problem of operating the system as an isolated unit in the nationwide set up." There was absolutely no benefit to be derived from amalgamation. After all, the telephone department was contributing revenue to the city coffers equal to five mills on the tax rate.

Ray Reierson, Telephones Minister, was asked to comment. He could see no reason why the two systems could not co-exist peacefully, but from an economic point of view it would be better for all concerned if the CTS joined forces with AGT. With amalgamation there would be no duplication in equipment or manpower, which would result not only in monetary savings but smoother operations. The question of costs was important at the time as there would be tremendous expense involved in providing links with the new long distance networks.

As luck would have it, this public comment came right on the heels of an AGT request for help from the city government. Some Edmonton residents were delinquent in paying long distance charges to AGT. Delinquent to the tune of $50,000 at that time. In the previous five years, AGT had written off $18,000 annually in accounts from Edmonton subscribers. The provincial department was asking Edmonton to help collect these overdue bills. If Edmonton helped AGT collect, the city would get one dollar for each disconnection and an equal amount for each reconnection.

At the time the only check the company had on delinquent subscribers was a no-toll tone attached to the subscriber's phone which would indicate to the long distance operator that the account was overdue. The operator would not put through any long distance calls from that instrument. AGT supplied city telephones with the equipment and paid them two dollars for each no-toll tone attached, but the tones only worked for calls originating from that phone. The wiley subscriber could use a neighbor's phone and charge it to his own account and the operator would have no way of knowing that the person was in arrears. Also undetected were incoming or reverse calls. Many habitual business abusers would escape having their long distance service cut off by changing names and opening new accounts.

Alderman Douglas wanted to know what AGT would do for city telephones in return. Discuss toll revenues for instance? The telephones minister said AGT was following standard North American practice in the matter. The local company would be paid a toll commission only if that company had performed a direct service in placing the call. When Edmonton subscribers placed long distance calls, the equipment and manpower used belonged to AGT. Mr. Reierson pointed out that AGT paid the city rental for the use of city telephone trunk lines from Edmonton exchanges to AGT equipment but he did end his statement by saying that AGT would "continue to study the matter with an open mind."

On January 11, the city by-laws committee recommended that the city not grant the request unless the provincial government system agreed to share their revenues. Mayor Roper, believing in "love thine adversary" rather than "an eye for an eye," asked the committee to reconsider. He felt that refusal to help AGT in the matter would close the door on the question of sharing toll revenue.

Telephones Minister Ray Reierson and Deputy-Minister R. S. Losie then appeared to the committee, saying that when trust is broken by a subscriber, the issuing company (city telephones) is "a party to the delinquency."

Council agreed to help AGT collect the overdue bills, with no strings attached. By-law 1915 gave the telephone superintendent authority to disconnect a city subscriber after 1) being notified in writing by AGT that the account was delinquent, and 2) giving the subscriber a 25-day grace period during which time he could pay his long distance bills. It worked: over half the accounts were paid in the first week!

After the by-law was passed, toll revenues and delinquent subscribers became yesterday's news and both camps were silent — for about eighteen months.

In October of 1961, AGT engaged the consulting firm of Sloan, Cook and Lowe of Chicago to study AGT and CTS to determine the degree of integration and the expenditures required to establish direct long distance dialling.

The question on everyone's mind was: did AGT have an ulterior motive? Was AGT going to buy CTS? The consultants would be studying the city system in detail, supplying AGT with figures on the estimated value of the city system.

Both AGT and CTS stated that there had been no negotiations nor were any planned. But speculation continued. In January of '62 Reierson said that the sale of CTS to AGT would result in a more efficient service for subscribers and a less costly service, especially with the problems "anticipated with the advent of direct distance dialling."

In February, AGT agreed to pay the city $60,816 for services and equipment provided in 1961 to AGT in the surrounding areas of Jasper Place, St. Albert, Sherwood Park and other outlying areas. When direct dialling between the city and these outlying areas was introduced, there would no longer be any method of counting calls between the city and the fringe areas. After some months of discussion, the two parties agreed on a basis of payment.

In August, there was a rumor circulating that the Chicago consulting firm had placed a price tag of $50 million on the city telephone system. Two months later Mayor Roper received the consultant's detailed report. After studying the report, Mayor Roper came to the conclusion that amalgamation would be advantageous for AGT but not for the city. He said that an AGT offer would be considered only if it included the projected growth and business worth of the city's telephone system. In 1961 alone, the system's net revenue was $2,696,639. The city wasn't too receptive to discussions aimed at depriving the city of that yearly revenue.

Deputy Minister Losie was also on the campaign trail. With the coming of direct distance dialling it would be necessary to incorporate some AGT and CTS equipment. This would complicate billing to a point that computers would be necessary. Losie also said there would be no reduction in staff if CTS were to sell, as the provincial department would assimilate the city employees.

Something would have to be decided soon! Direct distance dialling was on its way to Edmonton. Red Deer was connected in September of '63, Lethbridge would be connected by the end of the year, and Calgary, by mid '64. Edmonton was the last city on the list because, according to AGT general manager, J. W. Dodds, the difficulties in linking the two systems were causing a delay.

In February of '64, CTS was given approval for its 1964 capital budget of $4,063,240. C. E. Brown told city council that the system's capital expenditures over the next five years would soar as the system became more complex and technologically sophisticated. He said that a larger system would be able to absorb that extra cost better than a small system.

This statement sparked more questions concerning the possibility of a sale to AGT. Alderman Les Bodie wanted to see negotiations start, with a CTS price tag of $54 million. He could see no advantage in borrowing money to buy AGT's facilities in Jasper Place (which would cost about $4 million) when increased operations would mean increased costs. AGT was in a better financial position to shoulder the very large expenditures anticipated with direct distance dialling and the increasingly sophisticated and complex telephone equipment. The amalgamation would eliminate duplication and would give city telephone employees better career opportunities.

Alderman Weinlos was against selling the system, citing increased telephone revenues. In 1954 the revenue had been $124,000 and by 1963 the total had skyrocketed to $1,475,000.

In June of '64, Mayor Hawrelak formed a five-man committee to study the sale of the system to AGT. A year after the committee had been formed, it was still investigating. Les Bodie was still in favor of selling, referring to C. E. Brown's statement that the DDD costs would be tremendous and that at some future date the city system would be a liability instead of an asset.

In September the government announced construction that would increase AGT's office space 300 percent. The rumor resulting from that announcement was that AGT would construct a skyscraper in Edmonton as bait for the city to sell its telephone system. The building would be a combined AGT and CTS head office. All Edmonton would have to do was sell its estimated $65 million baby.

Mr. Reierson denied the rumors, stating that AGT had to expand as it was critically overcrowded. The government had chosen Edmonton as the site of AGT's proposed thirty-storey skyscraper, which would make it Edmonton's largest single office building.

Failing to enter into serious talks regarding buying and selling, AGT and CTS were co-operating in the installation of the DDD system by the end of the year.

In May of '66 the sell rumor surfaced again and this time the estimated value of CTS had risen to $90 million. Both Stan Hampton, CTS's new superintendent and J. W. Dodds, general manager of AGT denied the rumor, saying that the two systems were merely working closely together installing the long distance direct dialling system.

In June of '66 the proposed sale was again in the news. At a meeting of the East Edmonton Business Association, Mr. Reierson promised to do all he could to affect the merger of AGT and CTS. He again stressed the economic saving that would result from a merger. Money would be saved both in office space and phone equipment. One system could provide earlier modernization of facilities. Also, the city of Edmonton could retain the revenue collected from the city part of the system, which would keep the mill rate down as it had in the past.

The rumor machine was going full tilt that summer. The next bit of gossip it produced made a few folks snigger. The rumor that Bell Telephone Company of Canada was going to buy out AGT was short-lived.

Finally in March of '67 the city council decided not to accept an AGT offer to buy after studying a report prepared by Harry Rogers, chief engineer, Bert Billingsley, commercial manager, and William McLaughlin, plant manager of CTS. Although CTS faced spending an estimated capital of $41 million over the next five years, anticipated profits by 1972 would be over $4 million.

In 1967, CTS studied a proposed takeover of AGT's telephone facilities in Jasper Place, and a year later negotiations began. The city offered AGT an exchange of service areas. In return for telephone rights in Jasper Place, 'edmonton telephones' would allow AGT to service certain areas outside the city limits that were at the time served by 'edmonton telephones'. Since Jasper Place had been annexed to the city three years before, the city wanted to include the area in the city telephone network.

In the early part of '69 Edmonton's proposal was rejected by AGT and the provincial department submitted a counter-proposal to buy 'et'. Mr. Reierson felt that total ownership of the province's telephone network was more realistic than leaving just one area under municipal ownership. At the same time, the telephone minister declined to discuss the city proposal of sharing long distance toll revenues.

Alderman Crawford suggested an alternative to outright sale of 'et' or AGT's Jasper Place phone network. What about a joint AGT and 'et' administration of telephone operations in the Edmonton area? In return for that concession, 'et' would receive a share of the revenue from long distance calls originating in Edmonton and an initial share of funds arising from the equalization of capital costs. Mr. Crawford suggested a study committee be formed consisting of the 'et' superintendent, Edmonton's intergovernment officer and a member of the utility committee who would meet with AGT officials.

Alderman Ed Leger was quick to reject the proposal, saying that that would be akin to a "mouse sleeping with an elephant — constant danger." Mayor Ivor Dent agreed that 'et' should not consider a merger or a sale, citing the high property taxes which would be even higher if the revenue-producing utility were turned over to the provincial government.

At the end of July the government announced it would not sell the Jasper Place phone system to 'et.' AGT had bought land in West Jasper Place in order to expand its telephone operations. This decision may have been influenced by the fact that 'et' had requested $400,000 from AGT for the city's share of the long distance toll revenues. After AGT's refusal to sell the Jasper Place service, the amount demanded was reduced and resubmitted to the government. Again it was rejected.

By January of '70, 'et' was getting impatient. Alderman Tanner suggested that Edmonton tally the figures and send AGT a bill to cover 'et's' share of toll revenues for the past five years. Tanner suggested that Edmonton residents were subsidizing AGT subscribers to the amount of $5 million annually. Either the telephone minister and his assistant were not performing their duties properly, Tanner claimed, or they were deliberately penalizing the citizens of Edmonton. He suggested AGT pay 'et' twenty percent of the toll revenue on long distance calls originating in Edmonton.

The city sent the government a bill for $3 million and a letter which stated that the amount was conservative and was "subject to upward adjustment both from value and interest if not settled at an early date."

AGT had no intention of paying the bill: Edmonton already received $862,000 a year from the provincial body and there was no reason to increase that amount.

In March, the city decided to inform higher powers of its bid for justice. Eric Kierans, Federal Communications Minister, received a brief from the city stating that 'et' rates would be forced up if the city had to continue to subsidize long distance callers. The brief maintained that:

The continued rejection of the 'et' claim by AGT will perpetuate the inequitable subsidization by 'et' subscribers of all toll users not only in Alberta but also those toll users connected to the national and international communications network. Because of inflation and also because technological advancement has not significantly reduced the cost of local operations to the benefit of the local user, this subsidization of toll users must inevitably result in an increase in the local telephone rates for Edmonton telephone subscribers.

In the fall of '70, AGT and 'et' were engaged in a battle in the Jasper Place and West Jasper Place neighborhoods. Both 'et' and AGT were extending their facilities in the areas and it was getting to a point where jurisdiction would have to be given to either the city or AGT. The question was not "who should service Jasper Place and West Jasper Place," but "who should service new areas of the city?"

Premier Harry Strom demanded the city cease cable installations in West Jasper Place. AGT referred to a boundary agreement signed in 1963 by Mayor Elmer Roper and AGT general manager, J. W. Dodds, which stated that AGT had the right to serve all areas not included in the city's boundaries at the time. Strom also accused 'et' of refusing to co-operate in planning of trunking lines linking AGT's Jasper Place facilities with the city system.

Commissioner Stan Hampton stated that the city's new telephone by-law authorized 'et' to develop new areas of the city. It was logical that 'et' install telephone equipment in West Jasper Place as it was part of the city of Edmonton. Strom replied that AGT's position as a crown agency gave it the right to enter the city.

The city didn't agree with that remark and named a committee to negotiate with AGT for the right to service newly-annexed Edmonton subdivisions. Committee members Ivor Dent, Neil Crawford, Ken Neuman and Terry Nugent offered AGT all areas annexed west of 149 Street in return for all other new areas. Strom rejected the proposal.

The city then disputed the legality of the 1963 boundary agreement, claiming that the agreement had not been approved by the city. The city could not relinquish a franchise without a plebiscite. Strom threatened to legislate.

In January of '71, Alderman Tanner introduced a motion to borrow $16 million so the city could install its own long distance equipment, and make an application to the Trans-Canada Telephone System for membership.

Just at this time, a city resident gave notice of his intention to bring the city of Edmonton to justice for refusing to install a telephone in his home in Jasper Place. His case, to be heard before the Supreme Court of Alberta, would test the legality of the 1963 boundary agreement. AGT immediately offered Edmonton the right to supply the citizen with a telephone, but 'et' refused as it wanted the case to go to court. When it did, the 1963 agreement was ruled invalid because it hadn't been approved by council, the Public Utilities Board, and by two-thirds of the rate-payers. If AGT wanted the telephone rights in new areas of the city, it would have to legislate.

A poll of Edmontonians showed that 77 percent were in favor of a municipally-owned telephone system. A report prepared by the city telephone department stated that Edmonton's case was a case for all urban residents of Alberta.

... If Edmonton is stripped by legislation of these rights which have existed prior to the formation of the province and were confirmed when Alberta became a provincial entity, all municipalities will also have lost their right to serve their own citizens if so desired and if this is in their best financial and other interests.

In March of 1971, Premier Strom announced that the government would legislate. Talks betwen the two parties were terminated. Strom said that once boundaries were established through legislation, negotiations would continue. He also suggested a provincial plebiscite be held.

Shortly after Strom's announcement a motion condemning provincial legislation to limit 'et' expansion was unanimously endorsed by Locals 30 and 52 of the Canadian Union of Public Employees (CUPE), Local 209 of the International Firefighters Association, Local 569 of the Amalgamated Transit Union, Local 1007 of the International Brotherhood of Electrical Workers (IBEW) and Local 9-829 of the Oil, Chemical and Atomic Workers Union. Edmontonians were also organizing a protest march to the legislature.

That was too much for Strom. He agreed with Ivor Dent to leave the decision to a three-man arbitration board composed of AGT general manager J. W. Dodds, city utility commissioner, Stan Hampton, and Alexander Lester, a retired Bell Canada vice-president. In April, Strom announced that the government had decided against any telephone legislation that session and the board talks were postponed until the end of May.

During the provincial electioneering that summer, the Conservative leader Peter Lougheed said that if his party was voted into power, Edmonton would be allowed to expand its natural boundaries. In August, Lougheed formed the new Conservative government of Alberta.

Four months later the arbitration board came to the decision that 'et' should be sold to AGT. The city, not happy with the recommendation, immediately set up a three-person committee composed of Ivor Dent, Una Evans and Buck Olsen to negotiate with a cabinet committee consisting of Telephone Minister Len Werry, Labor Minister Bert Hohol, and Helen Hunley, Minister Without Portfolio.

This negotiating committee agreed, in the first month of '72, to let Edmonton service the new areas of Millwoods, Castle Downs and Kaskitayo, and to let the government service new areas west of Jasper Place until a permanent agreement was reached.

The jurisdictional war ended July 24 when city council accepted the government's offer to let 'edmonton telephones' expand within the city boundaries. The agreement between the city and province also contained the following points:

1. Both companies would serve customers within each other's areas where it was more economical and practical and at the request of the other company.

2. Further discussions between the city and province would seek ways of securing additional toll revenue from the TCTS.

3. The general managers of 'et' and AGT would continue to review inter-company charges for extended area service.

4. A single directory would be issued to include Edmonton and the surrounding areas.

AGT's facilities within the city boundaries would cost an estimated $3.5 million. Edmonton approached the Alberta Municipal Finance Corporation for a loan to buy out the facilities, but the city was turned down, forcing it to borrow on the open market.

By the beginning of 1973 city council was talking about setting up a long distance service in Edmonton. It voted to borrow $16 million to buy the needed long distance facilities, and to approach the

Trans-Canada Telephone Sytem (TCTS) for the right to provide long distance service. In two months Edmonton was informed that it wouldn't be allowed to provide long distance service because the city didn't have AGT's support.

The following year the city and province began negotiations to broaden the extended service area to include Calmar, Devon, Fort Saskatchewan, Leduc, Legal, Bon Accord, Morinville, Onoway, Stony Plain and New Sarepta.

Since the Conservative government had assumed power in '71, the city had been pressing for a share of the toll revenue but did not have any luck in coming to any agreement with the province. In 1975 the council thought of another way to squeeze the money out of the province. The economic affairs committee recommended that a 50 percent surcharge be put on billings for city telephone equipment used by the provincial government. This surcharge would equal the amount that 'et' would get from toll revenue. The suggestion was shelved in favor of continued toll revenue negotiations.

When the discussions were again resumed, Edmonton went to the table with a strong argument. Because 'et' costs and investments were not included in AGT's calculations for TCTS toll settlements, the people of Alberta were subsidizing the rest of the telephone users. If AGT would include 'et' investments and costs, AGT would get a larger share. It worked, for on December 14, 1977, city council approved a memorandum of agreement which gave Edmonton a percentage of TCTS toll revenues. This agreement was a result of a change in the method of determining toll revenues. Until 1976, the TCTS divided revenues only among its members; a fact that excluded Edmonton. The new formula allowed AGT to increase its TCTS share by counting 'et' equipment, therefore providing the city with a share of the revenue and increasing AGT's toll revenue.

After sixty years of dogged perseverance, the city received a beautiful cheque from AGT in the amount of $1,232,975.40 for its share of the 1977 toll revenue.

In 1978 AGT signed an agreement with Saskatchewan whereby that province would pay 50 percent of 'et's' share of the tolls for 1977, 60 percent for 1978 and an increase of 10 percent yearly until 'et' was getting 100 percent of its share from long distance calls placed to Saskatchewan from Edmonton subscribers. British Columbia agreed to pay 100 percent of the revenue share from calls to British Columbia from Edmonton, starting in 1978.

The estimated revenue from the Trans-Canada System, British Columbia and Saskatchewan for 1978 is $2,800,000. Edmonton had won its case. The mouse had roared!

The New Administration

On October 16, 1965, the city announced that Stan Hampton would become the new superintendent of the telephone department effective January 1, 1966, taking over from retiring superintendent C. E. (Buster) Brown. At the time, Hampton was the chief electrical engineer in the electrical distribution system. According to Mayor Vince Dantzer, the appointment was in keeping with the city policy of filling new positions with people already on the city staff, rather than hiring outsiders.

Hampton had a good record. He received a B.Sc. in electrical engineering from the University of Alberta in 1946 and joined city power in that year. In 1951 Hampton became chief engineer and remained in that position until his appointment as superintendent of telephones. He was a member and former chairman of the Engineering Institute of Canada.

There was probably some discussion within the walls of the department as to Hampton's capabilities in the area of telephones. He was somewhat familiar with the department, as the City Telephone System (CTS) and City Power worked closely together in co-ordinating plans and sharing some facilities.

It wasn't long after Hampton's takeover that the six hundred telephone employees became aware of a new force. Hampton swept in like a strong breeze, bringing many new ideas with him.

One of Hampton's first statements as superintendent was his belief that CTS should remain a municipally owned and operated utility because it was potentially financially successful. He felt that, because for years rumors of a sale to Alberta Government Telephones (AGT) had been discussed, city telephone employees were suffering from a loss of identity, spirit and pride. Also, public criticism of the department's efficiency had further undermined the telephone employees' morale.

Hampton wanted the telephone department to regain its pride and spirit, and its identity. To accomplish this he made several changes. He reorganized the department. New engineering and plant departments were created. The engineering department, headed by newly-appointed chief engineer Harry Rogers, was to concern itself with techniques, design of inside exchanges, outside plant, and types of equipment. The plant department, supervised by newly-appointed plant manager Bill McLaughlin, would be responsible for co-ordinating the operation of the facilities with the most efficient use of equipment, material and personnel. George Sloan succeeded Rogers as outside plant engineer, Graham Barker became central office engineer, Alf Want became systems planning engineer and Hugh Dunnigan was named customer services engineer. Fred Windwick was the new advertising supervisor and Wilf Kinney was promoted to assistant superintendent.

Hampton next tried to improve morale. He wanted to create a new logo for the department that would distinguish it as a utility separate from power, water and sanitation. Fred Windwick had the job of coming up with an identifying logo. He contacted Al Roberge of the William-Huff Art Studio and asked them to design a unique logo. The result, in use today on everything from company stationery to installation trucks, is the black and orange 'edmonton telephones' or 'et' name and logo.

This logo swept first place honors in the straight truck class for color and design in the 1968 National Private Truck Fleet Marking Contest sponsored by the Private Carrier Conference of American Trucking Associations Incorporated. The presentation was made during the conference's ninth annual mid-year meeting in Las Vegas, Nevada. At the Fleet Owners Conference in Chicago in April of 1968 'edmonton telephones' was awarded the Fleet Design Award for 1967. The awards are presented annually to selected companies in Canada and the United States whose vehicle colors meet the standards of excellence as set down in *Fleet Magazine* of New York.

Hampton made further changes. He promoted Fred Windwick to directory manager, and hired Brian Holmes as marketing manager and Al Bleiken as business information services manager. It was Hampton's intent to change the department from an organization that provided telephone service to one that provided total telecommunications service. He talked of inter-office communication and closed circuit TV, announcing that closed circuit TV would be installed in the library for security purposes. He spoke of future plans for "enter-phones" or devices which open apartment doors by regular telephone. Data transmission over telephone wires from central records would follow. By 1969 electronic switching would be replacing mechanical switching. The department would change from a company replying to customer demand to a company selling customers not just a telephone but an assortment of sophisticated telephone and computer equipment. The objective of 'et' would be to sell the customer the best telecommunications service available.

The training and safety sections were also studied, and their programs expanded. The present training program at NAIT for telephone craftsmen was a result of the efforts of Stan Hampton.

He effected another change. The title of the head of the department was changed from superintendent to general manager. It was also during Hampton's time that the department purchased its first bucket lift and installed its first cross-bar equipment.

In January of '67, Stan Hampton was named utilities commissioner, retaining the position of 'et' general manager until another man could be found. In '72 Hampton became chief commissioner. He retired from the city service in 1976.

In February the hunt for a new general manager began. The position was filled in August of '67 with the appointment of Doug Burrows, effective October 1.

Doug Burrows came to Edmonton from Winnipeg. He had been associated with the Manitoba Telephone System for thirty-one years, most recently as general staff engineer. In that position he was responsible for the engineering aspects of Manitoba Tel and in charge of three hundred employees.

Burrows had worked with Manitoba Tel as a student in the summers from 1936 to 1939. When the war started he joined the artillery unit of the army, advancing to the position of major by the time he returned to Canada in 1945. At this time he went to a Canadian army staff college, graduating with a degree in commerce. He also worked for Manitoba Tel during this time, becoming a full-time employee upon graduation from army college. Burrows stayed with the reserve army until 1967, at which time he was a colonel. During this time he served one year as aide-de-camp to Governor General Mitchener and two and one-half years as aide-de-camp to Manitoba's lieutenant-governor.

Burrows implemented other improvements in the department. AGT and 'et' were still embroiled in disputes, and there were still rumors of amalgamation. The image persisted of earlier days when telephone equipment was hard to get, and delays had resulted in public criticism. Burrows wished to eradicate the criticisms by making the department a smooth-running efficient machine.

Burrows did some further reorganizing. He instituted an employee level system, similar to that used by other telephone companies. Management was graded from one to five levels, with level five being the general manager. A system of advancement was instituted for labor as well as management.

He set down job specifications. At the time, personnel didn't have clear-cut responsibilities and some employees did some jobs not related to their particular position. With the new specifications, all employees knew their job descriptions, and therefore what was required of them.

Burrows expanded the telephone department from three to four branches, introducing the services department, now called organization, development and financial results branch (OD and FR). Paul Trawick was hired to head this department, initially to set up a uniform system of accounts and to develop productivity measurement plans.

Burrows started management training, sending the third and fourth-level personnel to the Banff School of Advanced Management. He established the Londonderry Training Centre in 1969 and 1970, which had training programs and short courses for plant craftsmen to supplement on-the-job training and NAIT or SAIT programs.

Previously, the training program received by telephone employees was only on-the-job training. An apprentice learned from one of the senior craftsmen, and so learned only that person's concept of the job. Magazines and books were available but not widely used.

Another training school was started for management shortly after the Londonderry training centre was started. It consisted of short courses on various managerial skills given by 'et' employees, and information on courses in the city which would be of benefit to employees.

Plant location records were set up. In the earlier days some records of assets were kept, but in many cases the records were carried in the memories of some of the employees. When these people left the department, they took with them maps of cable routes and other information — in their heads!

Burrows as a general manager believed in organization. He was interested in economy and efficiency — achieving the most efficient telephone system while utilizing the smallest possible amount of material and manpower.

In 1972 Doug Burrows was named utilities commissioner. Four years later he became the city's chief commissioner, the position he holds at present. The hunt was on again for a new general manager.

On February 22, 1973 the city announced that Jack Pulford, former manager for communications system sales for Northern Telecom, had been appointed general manager of 'et'. Pulford's career in telecommunications started in 1937 with Northern Electric when he worked as an installer in Quebec and Ontario. He joined the RCAF in 1941, returned to school in 1945 and in 1950 received his B.Sc. in mechanical and electrical engineering from the University of Toronto. From that time he held various management positions in Northern Telecom including sales manager for the Canadian marketing service division, sales manager in the switching division for Canada and the United States, and central office equipment group product manager.

Pulford's expertise was in marketing. His main objective as general manager of 'et' was to turn the department into a marketing-oriented company, that is, to go out and sell the customer on communications equipment supplied by 'et'. To achieve this purpose he did some reorganizing of personnel. Pulford believed an employee could be brought to his full potential if he was in the right position — a case of "putting the square pegs in the square holes and the round pegs in the holes."

He started a hiring campaign, enlarging the sales department in particular. To boost company morale and encourage team work he maintained an open door policy. Anyone, from a fourth-level manager to an apprentice cable splicer was welcome in his office. In a short while he knew the staff of over a thousand by their first names.

Pulford also had some ideas on training. To improve the knowledge and efficiency of the managerial force, he introduced a management trainee program called "management by objectives," holding classes in the evening for the management personnel. He also established familiarization classes open to all employees. Here people would learn what fellow employees did in their particular jobs and how they interacted within their department. He also campaigned to raise the managerial pay scale of 'et' to equal that in other telephone companies.

Jack developed and taught a new marketing format called IMPACTE, or "the individual's mental power applied carefully and tactfully with effectiveness." The format was based on the idea that everything worth-while in life must be sold. Pulford trained 110 'et' managers from Levels I to IV in this program, which had also been used to train Northern Telecom management. Under Pulford the marketing department was expanded and refined, paving the way for the future shift within the industry to a marketing-oriented position.

Jack Pulford was general manager of 'et' until he retired on March 12, 1976 for health reasons. While general manager, he also served as acting personnel manager for the city for six months. He served a term as chairman of the salary appeal board of CURA, an organization of city's management employees. He was also vice-chairman of communications for the '78 Commonwealth Games, and was the 1975-76 president of the Edmonton Chapter of the Northern Council of Telephone Pioneers of America.

While 'et' was looking for a new general manager, Paul Trawick, then plant manager, was the acting general manager.

In July of 1976 George Kendall Foster became the new general manager of 'et', bringing with him a great deal of experience in telecommunications. Foster had joined Maritime Telephone and Telegraph after graduating from Nova Scotia Technical College as a mechanical engineer in 1948. In two years Foster organized the new plant extension engineering department. He stayed with MT&T until 1968, serving in positions of outside plant manager, assistant chief engineer, and general plant manager. In 1968 Foster joined the Government of Canada's Department of Communications in Ottawa. From 1968 until 1973 he was manager of the planning and design division. In this post he negotiated with telcos concerning local service requirements in data and voice transmission.

In 1973 Foster became involved in setting telecommunications policies for Canada. This included interaction with provincial government groups and telecommunications companies in developing a terminal attachment program.

When Foster came to Edmonton he was impressed with the advances 'et' had made in systems, methods and procedures. The department was advanced in computerized record keeping, and had developed and was implementing the first computerized directory assistance and CSIS in North America.

Foster helped to end 'et's' isolation from developments in telecommunications. At the time 'et' had a service agreement with AGT, who in turn had a service agreement with Bell. Under the agreement 'et' paid AGT a yearly fee for access to Bell's information and educational services. Sometimes 'et' didn't appear to get the full benefit of these services.

In 1977 AGT cancelled its agreement with Bell, in turn leaving 'et' without this valuable information. That year Foster negotiated a service agreement with Bell. For a monthly fee 'et' would be given access to Bell's research, including educational programs, industry information studies, and practices and procedures. This information would enable 'et' to keep in tune and in time with the rest of the industry.

One of George Foster's present objectives is to do an in-depth study of the company's organization, to determine how best to ensure the highest productivity and profitability. The restructuring of the department could proceed on a product, geographical or a functional basis. Foster is now implementing a program of job rotation of managerial people to give personnel more understanding of other areas.

Another of Foster's objectives is to organize a public relations campaign for the department, to let the public know that 'et' is a modern efficient organization that provides the city with the best communications service and contributes to the city's wealth.

Foster saw one of his objectives, that of maintaining low telephone rates, partially realized in 1978. Under the existing fiscal policy, 'edmonton telephones' pays the city a revenue tax of 8 percent. In addition, the utility must make a 15 percent return on equity, of this, three-fifths (9 percent) goes to the city's general revenue with the remaining two-fifths (6 percent) being added to retained earnings. Although rates were designed only to meet this 15 percent requirement, until 1978 earnings in excess of this 15 percent were also treated as retained earnings.

In presenting the application for a rate increase in 1979, 'et' sought and won approval for the principle that the 15 percent on equity could be treated as an average figure, starting with 1978. This means that earnings in excess of those required in the current year can be carried over to help stabilize rates in following years.

At present, the service time for getting a telephone is six days. Foster would like to see that reduced to two or three days, but first some problems will have to be solved. For instance, the number of new phones installed as the city grows in size is only the tip of the iceberg. The number of people and businesses moving around within the city means that many more installations and removals must be made. For the yearly increase of about 35,000 phones that 'et' now has, the department has to install 280,000 phones and remove 245,000. Edmonton is a fast-growing, fast-changing and extremely mobile city. If the city reaches a plateau in growth or becomes more stable with respect to business and residential locations, that eight to one ratio should be decreased. Eventually this problem will be surmounted when the jack and plug phone exchange program is completed. A customer will then get a phone from the Phone Exchange, pay a fee, receive a new number, go home, plug it in and in most cases, have service within one day.

Foster is now on a "meet his people" campaign. Feeling somewhat isolated from his staff because personnel are spread out in twenty-four different locations, he has recently initiated weekly meetings with Fred Windwick, general plant manager, and the plant foremen, and will expand this to include the employees in other branches.

George Foster inherited an organization that has gone through dramatic changes in the past ten years. In retrospect, it seems that the three managers preceding Foster came to 'edmonton telephones' at just the right time, implementing the changes and programs most needed. Now it's Foster's turn, to improve the organization so it will be ready to enter the wired world of the 1980s.

Training

Prior to the sixties, there was only one way to learn about telephones — that was to go to work for a telephone company. Universities and technical schools trained electrical and mechanical engineers, but not skilled craftsmen. Even learning to be a switchman in one telephone company didn't prepare one to work in other companies, because the systems and methods were often totally different. There wasn't any accepted apprenticeship program in the telephone crafts, and there was no formal teaching of telephony at schools and colleges.

Today the Alberta Government recognizes people who have graduated from the NAIT and SAIT Communications Electricians course, or the provincial apprenticeship program, as journeymen craftsmen in four craft areas; construction, sustanatation, switching and toll. Unfortunately people with a similar level of competence and knowledge from on-the-job training and related courses cannot be recognized as journeymen craftsmen by the government because the province at this time has no journeyman exams which these technicians or any out-of-province technicians can take. This will probably change as more demands are made for governmental certification of standards.

At 'et' all craftsmen are recognized as apprentices or journeymen, even if they do not have certificates. Other companies may not call their craftsmen "journeymen," but they do have some sort of company grading system.

Today a person starting with 'et' can start as an "apprentice," and after a period of four or five years will be considered a journeyman craftsman. In earlier days, the 'et' apprentice learned the trade from one of the senior craftsmen, with the result that knowledge and procedures were not the same for all journeymen, or for all craftsmen.

When Christie was superintendent he set up a small library of telephone books and magazines to make outside material and up-to-date methods and knowledge available to his men. Brown continued the practice and also set up a safety and training position. In the sixties Alf Want, Herb Caldwell and Stan Hampton played a major role in setting up the communications electricians course at NAIT. AGT and 'et' representatives and the NAIT administration designed the telephony course that started in 1966. A person graduating from this NAIT course still required about two years of on-the-job training.

In 1966 Ken Stamp was training supervisor of 'et.' In 1967 he left to teach a course at NAIT, and returned to 'et' in 1968. While at NAIT he became very familiar with the courses offered at the technical school and knew which areas of telephony were stressed. A graduate from NAIT may be well versed in one craft but not in another. When Ken returned to the department he proposed an 'et' training program to supplement existing training at NAIT, SAIT and on-the-job training. The courses would make craftsmen so familiar with tools, equipment and practices related to their jobs that they would have confidence and be effective in their jobs.

In June of '68 Stamp met with Doug Burrows to discuss the possiblity of starting a program. Stamp did a survey of the department to determine which areas were in need of a training program. He conferred with the executive of Local 1007 of the IBEW and received their backing. He then was given the green light by the 'et' executive.

The first training courses were taught in September of 1968 in South Stores by Gerry Richter, who handled outside plant, Ken Stamp, who concentrated on line and station equipment and Al Perry who taught Automatic Number Identification (ANI) courses. When direct distance dialling equipment was installed ANI was done by machine and the ANI courses trained the craftsmen on how to maintain the machines. Perry travelled to the different exchanges instructing personnel on the equipment.

In January of '69 the training program got some funding, and space was allotted in the Londonderry Exchange. As the budget was limited, makeshift equipment was used. The first tables were newsprint-covered sheets of plywood supported by wooden horses. The training centre slowly grew during the next three years. Additional 'et', AGT and Bell personnel were recruited to teach various subjects and courses. Instructors would study information from other telcos and technical institutes on methods of training and subjects for classes. Instructors would also consult with other 'et' personnel with regard to areas where instruction was needed. In 1972 Ken Stamp left 'et' to teach a course on PABX's at NAIT and Roger Simkin took over the training centre.

At present 'et' has a four-year apprenticeship program. Many employees are graduates of the NAIT program in telecommunications technology. They are placed at the year three apprenticeship level. People hired "off the street" begin at a year one level.

The apprenticeship program at 'et' recognizes about eleven specialized divisions or crafts. Under the classification of installer and repairer are the following: line and station installer, line and station repairman, PBX installer, PBX repairman, PABX installer and PABX repairman, special services installer and special services repairman, the tester who works the test desk, cable splicers, linemen and switchmen.

Craftsmen are given courses in their chosen area. For instance a switchman would learn principles and concepts of telephone technology and study electricity and transmission. He would also be taught the historical methods of step-by-step, as well as the cross-bar and SP1 systems of today and the digital systems of tomorrow. All craftsmen are given a slide presentation and orientation talk developed by Ken Lewis and a foreman's course which includes managerial skills and organizational study to familiarize employees with all branches of the department.

An example of a first year training in line and station installation for a person "off the street" would start with one week in the field. The employee would then spend one week at the training centre for a basic installation course in residential and single line business phones. Later he would take a one-week course in climbing poles. As there is an art to climbing poles the boys are instructed on the proper way of starting, climbing and standing on poles. They practise going up and down the poles until they are comfortable with heights and balance. On about the third or fourth day of training, three linemen practise playing catch with a ball while up a pole.

The employee would also take a course in subscriber equipment and a two-day course in first aid and safety, which includes a St.

John's ambulance course and studying government safety regulations. This first aid course has had good results, both on and off the job. For example, in 1976 two 'et' employees, Albert Katona and Graham Moore, with the help of a student nurse were credited with saving the life of a sixty-nine year old man who suffered a heart attack in a tunnel under the University Hospital. The two employees were repairing some lines at the time. The man was kept alive for twenty minutes with mouth to mouth resuscitation and external heart massage until the hospital's emergency unit arrived.

At present, there are about ten instructors at the Londonderry training centre providing courses for more than eight hundred new and seasoned craftsmen. The instructors are usually 'et' people, foremen of various departments who take some time to teach specific courses. These instructors, together with Roger Simkin, set objectives for general courses and approve new courses. When new equipment is introduced to the department the engineers and instructors usually develop a short course on the operation and repair of the machine. Sometimes suppliers of equipment provide instructors. In June of 1979 the training centre was moved from the Londonderry exchange to larger quarters.

Not just craftsmen, but other 'et' employees benefit from training programs. George Witt is in charge of management training and new employee orientation sessions. He teaches courses and recommends courses within the community which would be of benefit to various departmental people. Management people attend courses outside the city as well, in particular the Banff School of Advanced Management. Courses offered by different companies, like Xerox, are given to 'et' people. Consultants get special training in economics and marketing, phone exchange people take courses in equipment, techniques and public relations, and office personnel and operators in new kinds of equipment. There are always some 'et' people taking courses, as part of the ongoing departmental education program to keep 'et' people on top of the industry.

Transponders

Transponders are remarkable devices, about the size of a one-pound box of chocolates, that could enable the city to read utility meters automatically. This would eliminate the door-to-door meter reader and result in a cost saving substantial enough to lower utility rates. The units would be mounted on the wall beside the utility meters and connected to the telephone system. A silent call (test train) from the utility company or the city would connect the apparatus to a computer which would read the meters, or a central office scanner would access the units and obtain the readings.

Reading meters automatically is just one skill of this remarkable device, pioneered by 'edmonton telephones' and Control Devices Limited of Edmonton. The transponder could also monitor signals for fire, smoke or burglary. It could connect and disconnect cable systems, telephones and power through remote control. It could automatically turn on or shut off your stove or your block heater in your car, or your lights. It would be more reliable and more versatile than the family watchdog and not as expensive to feed.

The idea for an automatic meter reading machine was born ten years ago. In December of 1969, the director of research and development for Northwestern Utilities in Edmonton and Canadian Western Natural Gas of Calgary, Mr. George Kellam, formed a committee to study the possiblity of developing a viable system of automatic meter reading over telephone facilities. One month later, representatives from 'edmonton telephones', Edmonton Water and Sanitation, Edmonton Power, Northwestern Utilities and AGT joined the study committee.

For two years the committee studied proposals submitted by various manufacturers. They were all turned down, either because of high costs of manufacture and operation or inefficiency. The various committee members then drew up an agreement in the fall of '71, assigning responsibilities and costs for a planned automatic meter reading field trial.

The responsibility of 'et' was to design, construct and test an automatic meter reading access circuit. The 'et' engineering department, led by Bruce Cleveley and Ken Laubman, designed and constructed an automatic meter reading access circuit. (In 1975 the city of Edmonton, on behalf of 'et' received a U.S. patent for this "method of reading remotely located meters.")

The committee then selected thirty homes in Westmount (a telephone step-by-step and cross-bar switching equipment area) for the field trail. A transponder unit attached in those homes enabled a computer at NAIT to automatically access the test network to obtain power, gas and water meter readings. During the field test, daily comparisons were made of the manual meter reading and automatic meter reading. The trial was discontinued on July 5, 1972, after a six-month test, due to poor performance of the transponder units.

The transponder was then redesigned and manufacturers were sought. By January of 1973, ITT Canada at Guelph, and Control Devices Limited and General Data Systems of Edmonton signed agreements with the committee to manufacture transponders. The equipment was tested for the first six months of 1973 in the meter shops of Northwestern Utilities, Edmonton Power, and Edmonton Water and Sanitation. For the remainder of that year, the equipment was tested by the city's Univac computer. The tests indicated that Control Devices and ITT manufactured units met the specifications of the committee. After a few modifications were made to the transponders, Control Devices was authorized to install the units in ten households. Again comparisons were made between automatic meter reading and manual meter reading. At the conclusion of the trials, the Control Devices units were approved by the committee.

The committee discovered that Automatic Meter Reading (AMR) was more reliable and efficient than manual meter reading. AMR read three meters accurately in eleven seconds and the transponder didn't interfere with the telephone system. The transponders were never triggered by speech, data or other forms of signalling during the test period. Five power failures occurred during the period and although the transponders were inoperable during the failure, no memory loss was experienced by the units.

In 1975 the committee decided to go ahead with further cost studies. In 1976 an amount of $126,000 was included in the 'et' budget to begin utilization of the chip technology, and council tentatively approved an amount of $450,000 to cover 'et' costs of the Millwoods transponder tests scheduled for 1977. In August of '76 Control Devices were awarded a contract worth $400,000 to build 2000 transponders for the Millwoods test.

Control Devices then started negotiations with the city for exclusive rights to the patent, and proceeded to refine the transponder from a multi-component solid state device through the technology of integrated circuits to chip technology. This chip technology would allow adding future capabilities such as remote burglary, fire and smoke detection, plus remote control of appliances.

Some delays were experienced in perfecting the chip technology and the 1977 test was delayed. During this time Omaha, Nebraska installed test transponders but they were about four times as large as the units made by Control Devices.

In 1978 the devices were ready, and in December installation of the transponders into 600 homes in the Millwoods area was started under the direction of Bob Gibb, with back-up support from Myron Solojuk's section in engineering. Three hundred units were installed in occupied homes and 300 in homes under construction.

The present unit has a standby power source which would permit the unit to operate through a power failure. There are five control units to turn things off and on, and it has eight alarm system inputs. The unit has peak power demand modules that store power readings taken every hour for a 42-month period. This enables power companies to predict peak power levels and obtain more power during those times. Once light load periods are determined, Edmonton Power could perhaps reorganize its rate structure, giving users lower rates for power consumption during low load periods. It would then cost the domestic engineers less money to do their washing and ironing at 11 PM rather than 11 AM. In some places in the United States, companies are regulating loads and conserving energy by a system of cutting off air conditioners to certain parts of cities during certain hours. The goal here is energy conservation.

A thirty percent saving of meter reading costs could be realized if the city were converted to the units. The cost of manual meter reading would rise as more personnel were hired to cover an ever-expanding city. Besides conservation of energy and money for utility companies, the benefits to the householder would be numerous. The bother of letting the meter reader in would be eliminated and utility costs would be lowered. The alarm inputs could be used for fire, smoke or burglary, and the control units could be used on lights or any appliance in the house. It could warm the car up on a cold winter day and have the coffee ready in the morning.

If the Millwoods transponder tests prove that automatic meter reading is reliable and inexpensive, a $12 million capital program could begin in 1980 with the installation of transponders in residences and businesses all across the city, and the entire city could be converted by 1985.

The New Role of Marketing

With the rapid development of telecommunications technology, by the 1960s telephone companies faced competition from data and interconnect companies. The threat of competition from companies like IBM and Xerox was very real and uncomfortably close. In order to compete with such giants, a good marketing program was necessary. Telcos had to change from companies dominated by engineers and craftsmen to companies guided by marketing expertise.

In 1967 'edmonton telephones' began to develop a marketing program. Stan Hampton hired Brian Holmes and Al Bleiken to set up a marketing department and develop a training program for marketing personnel. At the time, 'et' had only a very small marketing section. There were only three sales consultants — Wally Watt, Al Turner, and Ted Bennett — and they mainly handled orders over the phone. Customers would call in asking about new or specific types of equipment and consultants would answer their questions. It wasn't until after 1967 that 'et' set out to solicit business. From a 1968 staff of 3, came a staff of 7 by 1970, 50 by 1975 and 75 by 1979.

There were many hurdles in the change to a sales and marketing-oriented business. Since engineering and plant had dominated telcos for so many years, these groups were naturally wary of the new marketing-oriented breed. Many thought these untechnical people were intruding into areas they knew nothing about. And the history of such groups wasn't reassuring. The multitude of travelling salesmen jokes indicated society's regard for the salesperson. Only recently has the image changed from that of a con man to a professional business person.

Today many marketing planners and successful salespeople have extensive backgrounds in the business or industry they deal with. Many have college, technical school or university training. In order to identify and propose the best type of communications service for a customer's needs, a consultant must be familiar with the customer's business. Today's consultants specialize: one may service customers involved in the oil industry, another in real estate, and another in hotels and motels.

Today communications consultants are not only trained in marketing, they are knowledgeable about the communications industry and the equipment and services available. Today's successful consultants possess the four qualities necessary to produce a good marketing person: a good academic background to provide essential knowledge; the skill to apply that knowledge to gain invaluable experience in the marketplace; a good attitude to the profession and confidence in the product; and the ability to adapt to a changing world, which is now especially important in telecommunications.

Al Bleiken started a marketing plan in 1970 and during the following five years developed a marketing concept for 'et', a training program for consultants. Consultants received on-the-job training, were enrolled in appropriate courses throughout the city, took special courses through AGT and travelled outside the city to attend courses. Many took courses like the Xerox Professional Skills Program. They attended seminars sponsored by suppliers of various equipment. Not just consultants but all management people took a variety of courses designed to enlighten them in the skills of successful marketing, management and sales management.

Marketing plans were devised to suit the ever-changing conditions in Edmonton. With numerous new products and the resulting change in market conditions it was necessary to adapt quickly. Successful advertising techniques were developed; advertising plans developed a common objective and company image. After a plan was formulated and put into effect, it was constantly evaluated and adjusted.

To be successful, 'et' would have to supply its customers with communications equipment they could use and benefit from. There was no point stocking and selling gadgets which didn't benefit the customer. The department concentrated on building a good image and reputation within the community. Their goods and service had to be reliable as well as effective. The customer had to be assured of good service and prompt action if problems occurred. The telcos like 'et' already had one advantage over interconnect companies, and that was familiarity; the image and reputation of the telco was firmly planted in the area. To maintain its lead in the community, 'et' would have to provide reliable equipment and service and, above all, give the customer what he wanted and needed.

In 1973 'et's' first marketing plan was implemented. It was aimed at the residential customer, not so much to achieve an increase in sales volume but in an attempt to influence buyer habits. The campaign was aimed at generating sales on extension and decorator phones.

Through the efforts of Holmes, Bleiken, Burrows, Pulford and a great many other 'et' people, the department had a successful market image by 1975. By utilizing the latest marketing techniques and management and sales concepts, 'et' had gained the respect of the industry.

A major change in the early seventies was the establishment of phone stores. They were set up to bring better service to the public. A person could walk into a phone store and browse through the many telephone models offered. After selecting a model and paying the rental or purchase price, he or she could take it home and plug it into a jack in the wall to get instant telephone communication.

The industry, in developing the concept of phone stores, was searching for ways to satisfy the increasing customer demand for faster service, reduced service costs, discount rates and options to rent, lease, or purchase telephone equipment. Telephone labor rates were becoming so high that ways were sought to reduce that expense. The solution was in establishing a new method of connection — converting to jacks which would allow a user to plug in and unplug his phone and move it to different areas of the house.

Subscribers were also demanding different models of telephones. Decorator phones were gaining in popularity to such an extent that retail stores were doing quite a business. Although city policy did not provide for attachment of these instruments into the 'et' network, policing the situation was very difficult. About all the city could do was to compete with these retail outlets by giving the customer what he wanted.

In the summer of '72, 'et' offered decorator phones to the public. There was an antique candlestick, a French desk model and a contemporary model in an oak case. The subscriber would pay $10 for installation plus an additional monthly charge to cover high servicing costs. Rentals were $3.50 a month extra for the contemporary and French models and $2.50 for the candlestick. It had taken 'et' so long to market these phones because before '72, a manufacturer couldn't be found that produced high quality models.

In 1973 'et' set up a task force to study the feasibility of phone stores and the associated jacking system for Edmonton. The task force, consisting of Chairman Newt Graham, Ed Burchmore and Gus Graham, divided a study program into the areas of commercial, engineering, shop and finances. Information was sought from other telcos and different kinds of equipment were studied.

Many suppliers demonstrated and promoted their equipment, and the task force had to recommend which type to use. The first phone store in Hallandale, Florida was studied. In that city the premium set selection increased by 50 percent, touch button phone use increased 129 percent, customer revenue increased 64 cents per customer per month, costs were cut in order handling, repair visits were reduced, and 70 percent of installation visits were eliminated.

Once the concept was studied, a recommendation was made that the system be implemented, and a study was taken as to which area 'et' should choose for its pilot project. Jasper Place was chosen because there was so much activity in the area, it had a large concentration of people, and all income stratas were represented. Meadowlark Shopping Centre was chosen as the location for the phone store as at the time the mall was being enlarged and there was space available.

The study was presented to the executive but shelved for one year. The report was reviewed again in 1974, and at that time it was decided to proceed with the program, starting with jack conversion in Jasper Place. At this time Meadowlark Shopping Centre didn't have any stores available, so alternate locations were studied. Space was procured in Centennial Mall, which at the time was planning a substantial addition.

The jack conversion program started in Jasper Place in 1976 and installations in new construction started shortly after. The conversion crews would install up to four jacks per home at no cost, but the subscriber would pay for any additional jack outlets.

The first phone store in Edmonton opened its doors to the public on June 13, 1977. Ken Foster and Mayor Terry Cavanaugh were on hand for the official exchange opening ceremonies. J. Ford Advertising, and 'et', came up with the name for the store. The "Phone Exchange" was picked since the word "exchange" had always been associated with the telephone industry. Not to be ignored was the meaning that you could exchange one phone for another.

The new store, managed by Brian Strecker, offered the customer a choice of ninety types of equipment. There were princess, contempra and candlestick phones available in all colors, in a choice of dial or touch tone. Some had loud-speakers and logic diallers. Nightlite, wall hanger, logic 1, coin decorator, cradlephone, ericophone and chestphone were some other popular models.

People that had jacks in their homes could pick out a new phone, pay a rental fee, take it home and plug it in. A computer terminal located in the store was hooked into the city's Univac computer. A telephone number addressed to the computer would display the subscriber's name and address, and the number, model, color and rental fees of the phones in the home. With each rental the new information would be fed into the computer.

Customers were also able to pay their utility bills at the Phone Exchange, request power and water service, and have their phone repaired. If a phone was faulty the customer could take it into the phone store where the resident repair person could fix it. If the job was small, the customer could watch his phone being fixed; if it was a major repair job, the customer would be given another phone until his set was repaired.

In 1978 there were two exchanges — the Centennial Mall Phone Exchange supervised by Marj Henderson, a fourteen-year veteran in repair and dispatch, and the Kingsway Garden Mall Phone Exchange, supervised by Gloria Van Helvert. The Phone Exchange people were specially trained for their positions. In order to work in the store the personnel must be skilled in public relations and sales, have a knowledge of computers, technical knowledge of the equipment and secretarial skills. They are also given appropriate courses.

The Phone Exchange stores and jacking system have been popular with 'et' customers. On Thursday evenings and on Saturdays, the "phones go like crazy" says Marj Henderson, and June to September are the busy months. It's not uncommon for women to come into the store with a piece of fabric to find a phone to match.

In May of '78, the Centennial Phone Exchange had 1646 service orders, most of which were adding extensions, and replacing or exchanging phones. In one month telephone repair person Judy Moore handled 206 minor repairs in addition to checking and testing equipment.

From October of 1976 to November 30, 1978, 'et' had converted 62,829 housing units to the jack system, 9075 units higher than forecasted. This represents about one-third of the conversions required in Edmonton. The capital investment for the conversion project to November 30 was $547,000 less than was forecasted. The average increase in revenue for conversions to in-service customers was 46 cents per month, also more than predicted. It is estimated that 13,730 installation field trips have been saved and 3162 repair field trips saved, which amounts to a saving of $333,000.

Three exchanges are scheduled for 1979 openings. Petrolia and Millbourne Phone Exchanges will open in March, and another exchange in the Northtown area will open later in the year. The jacking conversion program is scheduled for completion in 1981.

The Phone Exchange concept will be enlarged in the future to include the imagination line of telephones, including such models as "Snoopy" or "Mickey Mouse" phones. Future plans include selling the equipment to the customer. Many payment plans along with manufacturers warranties are envisioned. The responsibility for upkeep of the equipment will be the customer's, and 'et' will realize a saving in repair costs. People who abuse equipment will be the ones who will bear the costs.

The Phone Exchanges will be retail outlets for communications equipment. The equipment available, whether it be an ordinary white desk phone or a complicated home computer, will be of the best quality available. Customers will be able to choose equipment that best satisfies their needs.

Into the Seventies

The key word of the seventies was "cable." Not the 2400-pair type, but co-axial cable. Cable — hopefully city-owned and operated — that would bring Edmontonians about twelve TV channels. Edmonton's third submission to the Canadian Radio and Television Commission (CRTC) was scheduled to be heard on April 28, 1970 in Calgary. It asked that 'et' be permitted to operate a co-axial cable distribution network.

It was the city's third bid for cable. The first submission asked that 'et' be permitted to operate a microwave circuit to pick up United States' television programs at the border, then distribute them in Edmonton through co-axial cable. The CRTC said it was against government operation of cable TV. The city presented another submission which replaced 'et' with a private company. The CRTC ruled against microwave pick-up of United States' programs.

In May, 'et' allocated $55,000 to cover costs of providing Edmontonians with television cable facilities. The cable would be buried in the ducts with telephone and power cable, and 'et' would be supplying these facilities whether or not the city was granted a cable license. If a private company won the cable battle, they would provide connection from 'et' cable to the home or office.

In October a four-company cable TV consortium, which included QCTV and Capital Cable TV, asked for the right to operate cable TV in Edmonton. The two companies would join with two Calgary firms in sharing the microwave from Trail to Calgary and Edmonton. Mr. Polanski of QCTV was confident of a judgement in the consortium's favor as cable TV costs would be reduced and the microwave facilities would be conserved if the consortium was granted permission to operate the cable. The microwave spectrum was almost at a saturation point at the time.

By May of '71 Polanski said the CRTC wouldn't permit a telephone company to have access to a cable TV system as a private utility company could provide the service at a lower rate. In that year, QCTV and Capital Cable made an agreement with the city. The companies would build the cable system, then when legislation was passed they would turn the ownership over to the city. The city suggested it be given the cable by 1982. The Social Credit government had said in 1971 that it would pass an order in council clearly setting out the city's right to own cable. The Conservative government agreed to do the same. The government then delayed its decision because ownership of cable was an issue across the country. The Conservatives said they would act on the matter once a national policy had been evolved.

In 1970 Canada was again a leader in number of phones per person — 43 for every 100 Canadians. Edmontonians were informed that their phones would cost them more money. If phone bills weren't paid by the due dates, a six percent interest fee would be charged. By April of 1971, the city of Edmonton would issue only one bill containing charges for telephone, power, water and sewer.

The touch button phone total in Edmonton had reached the 4000 mark and during the three years of their use in the city, maintenance costs were lower than those of dial phones. Touch button phones also proved more reliable in adverse weather conditions. The Westmount, Londonderry and Central exchanges were ready for the expected coming of picture phones. Doug Burrows reminded city residents that because of 'et's' contribution to the city coffers through revenue taxes, realty taxes and profits, the city mill rate was reduced six mills, which resulted in an approximate saving of $36 per household. Between the years 1965 and 1969, 'et' had contributed a total of $18 million to the city revenue.

In December '70, the Edmonton Chamber of Commerce asked that 'edmonton telephones' be the subject of an independent study. Because of the Alberta Government Telephones (AGT) and city dispute over servicing the area, the Chamber of Commerce wanted to know for sure how profitable the city system was and if residents would get a better deal being served by 'et' or AGT.

In 1971, 'et' introduced the busy signal verification service, and the first electro-mechanical common control system known as the Number Five Crossbar was installed in the Westmount Wire Centre. This system provided technological improvements like touch button calling, wide area telephone service and line link pulsing. The system was suited to data transmission and it could trace calls and record trouble information. It also had line load control which could be used in emergencies.

September 13 was the official opening day of the new main wire centre on 104 Street and 104 Avenue. The 72,000 square foot building had a lot of interesting features. It was one of Edmonton's and western Canada's first landscaped offices. The office space, instead of having a multitude of enclosed rooms, was instead divided by movable colored partitions. With this system the room arrangement could be changed in a few minutes; the plan provided for good space utilization and it was economical and flexible. One drawback was the lack of privacy. The 'et' personnel in the CN Tower and some staff from Churchill Square were moved into the new building. The exchange housed the city's second common control switching system with a line capacity of 90,000, which was not expected to be fully utilized until 1981.

Alberta's first centrex system was also installed by 'et'. It was specifically for large customers. The centrex system installed for the telephone department had 1450 centrex lines, 1150 key phones connected to 1A2 transistorized circuits, 1000 phones of other types, 130 call directors, 96 special sets for service representatives, 4 service representative monitor consoles, and 4 service observation consoles. That fall the second centrex system was installed for the Government of Canada's facilities in Edmonton.

The following February, Doug Burrows, 'et' general manager was elected to the board of the Canadian Telecommunications Carriers Association, representing the Independent Telephone Companies of Canada. Later in 1972, the city council's legislative committee recommended that Burrows be named utilities commissioner to fill the position vacated by Stan Hampton when he became chief commissioner.

In the summer of '72, a serious topic of conversation in 'et' offices was the implementation of a charge for directory assistance calls if the number asked for was already listed in the book. An amazing 80 percent of directory assistance calls fell into that category. It was suggested that a 25 cent charge be levied. Exceptions to the rule would be calls from pay stations and hotels where books were missing and from persons who were blind or otherwise handicapped. In 1971, the cost of directory assistance was about $800,000, and 130 operators were employed in the department.

In January of '71 the directory assistance operators answered 40,000 calls per day. The department was studying the Quebec Telephone System, which had been levying a 25 cent charge for unnecessary calls to directory assistance, for three months. During that time directory assistance calls to Quebec Tel had been reduced by 50 percent. Another study group was formed by 'et' to explore the problems involved in levying a 25 cent directory assistance fee. One of the biggest problems would be in deciding who would and wouldn't be charged for the service. If implemented, the directory assistance fee would not be put into effect until the system could be computerized, probably around the latter part of '73.

In late summer of '72, a contract was awarded for a $1,452,000 wire centre in Millwoods, which included 4800 lines of electronic switching equipment. Another contract for additional equipment for the main wire centre was awarded. Near the end of the year, a centrex was installed at city hall and one was installed for the city police.

Edmonton learned that it would be the host city for the '78 Commonwealth Games. The news was released in October during a five-hour toll call from Edmonton to the Canada Room in the Arabella Hotel in Munich. The entire call was broadcast to the media representatives in the Macdonald Hotel and crowds gathered outside. Ken Parsons, an 'et' employee, had set up a special assembly amplified phones system to allow the call to be broadcast. The Munich Telephone Company was not able to provide conference facilities in Germany so 'et' sent to Munich a completely wired 3A speakerphone, modified by Parsons, as well as an adapter to convert the European 220-volt circuit to 110 volts and a European adapter for wall sockets. The call cost $147 per hour. Other 'et' people involved in the project were Jack Laurie, Bob Gibb, Bob McCue, Paul Clarke and Jim Barry.

That year, Alf Want co-ordinated a nation-wide project for the Northern Council of the Telephone Pioneers of America. "New eyes for the needy" was a project in which old eyeglasses were collected and distributed to people in third world countries.

Two 'et' employees started a project of their own — an 'et' hockey club. Ken Parsons and Dale McIlhargy recruited enough sharpshooters to form two hockey teams to play "just for fun." According to early reports the players fell far short of NHL standards. (The team probably should have enlisted the aid of 'et's' Wayne Tennant, coach of the Edmonton Oil Kings. Another 'et' employee, Don Phillpotts, probably could have taught the fellows a bit of fancy footwork. Don is a holder of a fourth-degree black belt in karate and one time Alberta and western Canadian champion.)

Team members were allowed to body check "as long as it was confined to leaning against one another for support." When asked if the games would be open for the public, the players replied in the affirmative, saying that cheering fans and spectators were "often required to help the players from the ice." The teams must have improved their act, or at least enjoy the comic relief, for they are still on the ice.

On January 1, 1973, 'et' completed the takeover of AGT's telephone network in Jasper Place and West Jasper Place and many AGT employees in those areas joined the city telephone department. The city gained about 18,500 business and residential lines and about 27,000 telephones. At the time 'et' was also given the responsibility of providing telephone service to Millwoods, Castle Downs and Kaskitayo.

The next month the department's repair shop constructed and installed a vote recording system in council chambers in city hall. The system included display boards, relay equipment, voting buttons at each member location and a control panel console at the city clerk's desk. The system, first of its type and complexity, was the first step in installing a completely automated system which would record minutes, votes and attendance. The system was designed by Ron Sollanych and built by Charlie Eastaugh, Leo Benoit, Ken Bailey, Percy Coggles, Dave Mitchell, George McEwan and Ross McCutcheon.

That year 'et' took over administration of the radio section and control of the emergency call box system from the city engineering and transportation department. The 250 emergency call boxes in the city were connected directly to the fire department's emergency board in the communications building. The radio shop started in '56 with 180 mobile radios; in 1974 there were over 1000 mobile radios and 12 distinct radio systems.

In March of '74, the directory assistance abuse situation was so dire that 'et' launched a campaign over radio and TV stations to encourage people to first look in the telephone book for numbers before calling directory assistance. If that didn't work, then perhaps the implementation of a fee would be necessary.

Early in '74, 'et' was again behind in installing telephones. Part of the reason was due to the national rail strike the previous summer and a strike at Northern Electric which resulted in a shortage of equipment. Another reason was the extremely transient nature of Edmontonians. It wasn't uncommon for people to move three or four times a year. This resulted in a great number of installations and removals but no actual telephone gain. The department was spending a great deal of money accommodating the mobile population and it was getting no revenue for its efforts.

In the new construction area new switching equipment was planned for Londonderry, Lendrum and Bonnie Doon wire centres, and 28,400 lines of SP1 common control switching equipment was to be installed in the Main, Jasper Place, Mill Woods and Castle Downs exchanges. Two new wire centres were planned for '74 construction, one in Castle Downs at 113A Street and 162 Avenue at a cost of $600,000 and another at 104 Street and 83 Avenue.

New telephone equipment offered to the public that year included a system called call waiting, that beeped a conversation when another party was trying to get through. The system allowed a person to put his party on hold and talk to the person who just called in. Other new systems were call forwarding, which enabled calls to be transferred to another number where the person could be reached; speed calling in single or two-digit dialling; and three way calling that allowed a third caller to be brought in on the line.

In June, council approved a budget of $1.6 million to extend toll-free direct dialling to Calmar, Devon, Fort Saskatchewan, Leduc, Legal, Bon Accord, Morinville, Onaway, Stony Plain and New Sarepta by November of 1975. The extra charge to Edmonton residents for EFRC (Extended Flat Rate Calling) was $1.20 a year for residential phones and $2.40 per line for businesses.

Jack Pulford was concerned about the department's security at this time and asked Herb Caldwell, then safety and security officer, to conduct a security study of the department. As security was found to be poor, 'et' planned to install an adequate system. Various security systems were investigated, and 'et' became the first telco in Canada to install an extensive electronic security system.

A Rusco security system was installed to control access to various department buildings. All 'et' personnel were issued cards that would be inserted into Rusco readers placed by the building entrances. These readers were connected to the system control centre. Individual cards were coded so that the person could get into only those buildings he needed access to in the course of performing his duties. Top level management had access to all 'et' property. Because of the enormous amount of expensive switching and other equipment in wire centres, the buildings remained locked twenty-four hours a day; office buildings automatically locked at the end of the workday. If a card was lost or stolen or the employee quit, his card was immediately cancelled in the control centre. The cards eliminated the bother of keys and the danger of keys being duplicated, as these cards would be virtually impossible to duplicate.

On October 23, Mayor William Hawrelak and acting general manager Stu Baptie installed the three-hundred-thousandth phone in the city in the residence of Douglas Puffer.

A number of 'et' employees saw their work enable Geoff Taylor, a quadraplegic, to use a telephone. The system, modified and assembled by 'et' shop personnel Paul Swearing and Charlie Eastaugh, consisted of a speaker phone and dialler fitted with leavers mounted on a sewing machine cabinet. Gus Graham designed the system, Lil Whiteside programmed the dialler and trained the family in its use, and Gene Brenda and Dennis Bergson installed the system. This action came about when the Canadian Paraplegic Association asked Bob Kawchuck, 'et' co-ordinator on the Canadian Telecommunications Carriers' Association National Committee on Communications for the Deaf, if 'et' could develop a system that would allow Mr. Taylor to use the phone.

In 1975 a centrex was installed for the provincial government in 'et' offices. In this system the public would phone one number, called the RITE number (427-2711), and be connected with the right branch of the government. In March, 14,700 new lines were installed in the main exchange along with what was reputed to be the world's largest centrex system.

On June 1, Edmontonians could dial "911", "611" and "411" free of charge from outside pay phones. Before the coin-free calling was instituted, users would have to insert coins in the pay phones to make the call, but upon completion of a call to any of the three numbers, the money would be returned. This new coin-free service was eventually extended to include all pay stations in the city.

In April of '76, 'et' installed its first SL 1 PABX system in the offices of Syncrude Canada in the Petroleum Plaza Building. In June a second SL 1 PABX was installed at Associated Engineering Services. In this computer controlled digital transmission system, the voice sound was translated into mathematics and sent over the line where it was decoded into analog at the other end.

In May, 'et' introduced radio pocket pagers called beepers. These small electronic instruments, which could be attached to a person's belt or put in a pocket or purse, would beep when a person in the city was calling that person's seven-digit number. On the first day the beepers were introduced, the department issued over 200 at a yearly rental of about $300 each.

In the summer of '76 Wolfgang Blankeneau of the plant department went to the Montreal Olympics. He was a member of the Canadian Handball Team.

On February 15, 1977, 'et' became the first telco in Canada to offer its subscribers the latest package digital solid state stored program PABX or GTD-120. Another new machine on the market that year was causing a number of people some annoyance. Retailing for $264, the sequential telephone dialler could be hooked into the telephone line and programmed to dial up to 1000 numbers automatically. The persons called were then subjected to a recorded message. Although these calls were extremely annoying to most people, there were no specific regulations against the practise of trying to sell through personal or recorded telephone messages. however 'edmonton telephones' said it would investigate if a caller complained that he had received two or more calls in a short space of time.

In 1978 police were concerned with the number of nuisance calls coming into "911," and 'et' was concerned with the number of calls coming into "411." Again a surcharge of 25 cents was proposed for unnecessary calls to "411." People exempt from the charge would be the elderly and the handicapped. There would be no charge levied to persons calling from hotels, motels and phone booths, who may not have access to a telephone directory. Officials estimated a saving of $4 million would be realized in the space of five years. In 1977 it cost 'et' 29 cents to process one directory assistance call. In April of '78, it cost 31 cents, or a total of $2.5 million a year. Sask Tel was the only Canadian telco which didn't have a directory assistance charge. organizations for the handicapped had been contacted by "et." They developed a certification program exempting the handicapped from the charge. One 'et' official said that the charge was to eliminate charging all subscribers for the service abused by just a few. The proposition to charge 25 cents for each unnecessary call was passed by council in February, and went into effect July 1.

In 1978, 'et' had a capital budget of $51.7 million. This included $770,000 for monitoring equipment which could determine if a caller was using a pay phone booth or a location exempt from the 25 cent charge, or if he was phoning from a residence or business establishment not exempt from the directory assistance charge.

Also included in the budget was $12.4 million for outside plant equipment, $16 million for central office equipment and $19 million for customer equipment. Included in central office equipment expenditures would be a total of $3 million for the sophisticated CALRS system designed by Bell Northern Research. The system, to be operational by the spring of '79, is a computerized testing system. by punching a telephone number into a computer, an operator will be able to determine what, if anything, is wrong with the subscriber's phone. This eliminates the operator writing a repair order then having dispatch send a crew to the location. Bell Telephone and 'et' were the first telcos to purchase this type of equipment.

By 1978 Calgary captured first place from Edmonton in number of phones per person. Edmonton had 79.3 phones per 100 persons. Toronto placed third. Telephone installations averaged about 30,000 a year, at a time when population gains were 10,000 a year.

This was also the year of the 1978 Commonwealth Games. A number of 'et' people were involved in making the games a success. Bruce Cleveley, a veteran of '50 and 'et' transmission engineering supervisor, had been involved in the games since 1973 and played a major role in its organization. Bruce was asked to travel to New Zealand in 1973 to study the telecommunications system for the games in Christchurch. In June of '74 Bruce joined the full-time staff of the '78 Games as communications comptroller, working with the volunteer committee planning and budgeting for the required technical facilities.

Bruce was one of the Foundation's representatives on the city's management advisory committee which planned and controlled construction of the facilities required to host the Games. He was sent to study sports facilities in Edinburgh, London, Munich, Bienne, Paris, Tokyo, Mexico City and Montreal.

In 1977 Bruce became executive assistant to Games President Dr. Maury Van Vliet and was appointed a member of the four-man foundation management committee. Larry Samoil of 'et', a three-year volunteer on the communications committee, took over the post of communications comptroller and directed the final ordering and control of all technical facilities.

Equipment supplied to the Games by 'edmonton telephones' included 1500 centre telephones, 892 leased line pairs and 55 private lines.

Nellie Anquist, chief operator, had a staff of twenty operators working out of Churchill Square for the Games. Sixteen operators were hired on a part-time basis and four 'et' operators — Mary Brown, Audrey Kindley, Audrey Welby and Laurie Roester — were transferred to Games duty.

Other 'et' personnel involved in the Games included the following: Red Walker, commonwealth stadium; Brian Holmes and Brian Gibson, aquatic centre; Bob Garnet, leased lines and telephones; Don Barry, village communications; Bill Handley, media; Bob Johns and Bill Lobo, timing and results; Bo Van Beckel, boxing; and Howard Coram. Bob Garnet and Bob Johns worked during 1978 on a full-time basis. Ken Foster served on the '78 communications executive committee. Members of the '78 co-ordinating committee were Bob Garnett, Jack Christensen, Pug Young, Jim Searle, George McFarlane and Denys Lewis. The 'et' representative on the city's '78 Games committee was Bob Kawchuk.

Later in the year, 'et' began to promote the department's upcoming 75th anniversary, which would begin January 1, 1979 and end on January 1, 1980. On December 11, 'et' installed the four-hundred-thousandth telephone in the city at the temporary location of Santa's Anonymous at 10035 - 108 Street. Mayor Cec Purves made the final line test on the white Logic 1 before handing the receiver to Santa's Anonymous co-ordinator Stan Ravndahl. It had taken 65 years to install the two-hundred-thousandth telephone in the system. Less than 10 years later 'et' installed the four-hundred-thousandth telephone in the system.

The seventies also saw a number of new employees come into 'et' ranks who were destined to become senior managers.

William Dubik was with AGT for ten years prior to joining the city department as an engineer in the plant extension section. Bill is a University of Alberta graduate in electrical engineering. Bill, now outside plant engineering manager, does carpentry work in his spare time and builds stereos and TVs from kits.

Howard Johnson, corporate planner in OD and FR, worked at Ford and General Motors before moving back to Edmonton. Howard received a degree in mechanical engineering from the University of Alberta and a Master's in Business Administration from McMaster University. He also joined 'et' in 1972.

Tom Burns, manager of financial results and control in OD and FR, joined 'et' in '73 as a stationery clerk. Tom received his commerce degree from the University of Alberta and is now working on his RIA. Tom is a sharp-shooter on the 'et' marketing and city finance hockey teams, and enjoys trail riding in the summer.

Brian Gibson, Director of Sales and Marketing, joined the city in '74. He received a degree in commerce, then worked for the Bank of Montreal before joining 'et' as a sales manager in major accounts. Brian moved to the business service centre as unit manager, then became market planner in business. Brian, a downhill and cross-country skier, was involved in the Commonwealth Games in '78 as communications manager for the aquatic centre.

Yost Van Schaik, Indonesian-born University of Alberta arts graduate and now director of forecasting, joined in '74, as did Dave Rose, director of commercial methods. Dave had been in the Canadian Army in Germany and in the reserves for a number of years. He was associated with AGT for eight years before coming to 'et'. Dave is a director of the Staffordshire Bull Terrier Club in western Canada and owns a champion.

Bill Faist, director of business sales and service, also started in '74 as a project manager. Faist, a native of Austria, was educated in mechanical engineering in Vienna. He worked for Northern Telecom in various Canadian centres for eighteen years before joining 'et'. Bill is recognized as one of the best transmission and systems men in Canada.

In the summer of '78 Bob Hoy transferred from the city personnel department to 'et' as manager of the personnel services section. Bob, a University of Alberta graduate in commerce, was labor relations supervisor in city personnel.

Edmonton's telephone department has an exchange system with other city departments. At present Jack Thubrun is on a two-year loan from 'et' and is executive assistant to Commissioner Walker. other city employees previously in 'et' are Reg Bird, Al Crowley and

Ian Fraser, executive assistant to Chief Commissioner Burrows. Through the years 'et' has also had people on loan to Bell Canada. Lyle Laird was on loan to Bell and situated in Saudi Arabia until the beginning of 1980.

One department of 'edmonton telephones' that has always received a lot of publicity is the traffic department. From the first "hello girls" in the 1890s to the first information and repair operators in 1908, to the information operators of 1979, there has always been a certain romanticism about the career of a telephone operator. Surprisingly, the basic job hasn't changed much in those years. Just as a 1908, the '79 operator might be asked: "How do you bake a lemon meringue pie?" However the equipment used to answer the same questions has changed through the years. Today an ear plug and a computer terminal have replaced headphones and whirling directories or phone books.

There are now about 120 people in the directory assistance section, headed by Nellie Anquist, chief operator. Reporting to her are 5 group chief operators, or communications administrators as they are now called. Reporting to them are 1 or 2 supervisors who supervise the work of 20 to 30 operators. The operators work in 5, 6 or 7 - hour shifts, usually with a break every 90 minutes. Before 1968, women were not allowed to work past 11 PM. In that year the rule was abolished and now they work around the clock. The work is hard and the section experiences a large turnover of personnel. The operators handle local service as well as operator intercept for disconnected numbers.

Now, instead of having to look up numbers in a special book, the operators have 48 terminals or cathode ray tubes which are hooked into the city's Univac computer (affectionately known as Fred) which contains names, addresses and phone numbers. Since the 25 cent charge was introduced on unnecessary "411" calls in July, the number of calls has declined, but the operators still handle from 32 to 36 thousand per day.

About 20 percent of "411" calls are people asking unrelated questions like "What's a good restaurant?" The myth that the information operator was a brimming fountain of knowledge was still alive and well in the seventies, but the operators did get some relief when the name was changed from "information" to "directory assistance."

In 1978 the operators had a contest to choose a "411" ambassador to Klondike Days. During the festivities, Miss 411, Carrie Paproski, and her court attended functions throughout the city. The entire department took a more active role in Klondike Days in '78, holding its own Klondike breakfast for about 700 people, and providing the telephone number 471 - K Days, which was an 'et' service listing all the activities happening throughout the city during the festivities.

The Telephone Society, so active in the twenties, experienced a rebirth in the fifties and sixties and is again very active. About two-thirds of 'et' employees belong to the society, which throughout the year sponsors dances, barbecues and an annual retirement banquet in November to honor all the year's retiring personnel. The hard times dance usually attracts a large crowd dressed in their best destitute clothes. The yearly Christmas party for telephone employees' children aged ten and under has become so large that it is now held at the Kinsmen Field House. The children still get presents from Santa, and hot dogs and pop are served.

To be an executive in the telephone society the candidate must service time on the various committees then go from treasurer to secretary and up the ladder to the top. If the life of an executive appeals to him, he can start the whole process all over again. This way a number of people get experience and the executive is always changing.

The year 1979 is not only the 75th anniversary year for 'edmonton telephones', but it is the city's anniversary as well. Fred Windwick of 'et' is chairing a committee of citizens planning the 75th anniversary celebrations, 22 sub-committees were formed and each group is responsible for organizing various activities and events. one of the activities planned is "anything goes" competitions among various community groups in the city.

The Heritage Festival for 1979 will have the 75th anniversary as a theme; NAIT will be holding open houses comparing training facilities of 1904 and 1979; VIP banquets are planned; retired teachers will be visiting the schools in the city teaching the history of Edmonton. There is a plan to recreate the first city council meeting of 1904. The entire year is designed to be one memorable twelve-month-long celebration.

Looking into the next decade the telephone department is working on its five-hundred-thousandth telephone, which at the present growth rate of 30,000 installations a year should come early in 1982. The 1979 basic residential phone rental rate of $6.40 compares favorably with the '78 rates of $9.25 in Vancouver, $8.55 in Montreal and Toronto, and $7.50 and $6.10 in smaller cities. As well as having low rates, 'et' can boast a sizable profit every year. advanced digital switching equipment will be replacing some of the equipment presently in the wire centres, and in all likelihood fibre optics will be installed in the system. Three more Phone Exchanges are scheduled to open in '79 with 1981 the proposed date for the city's complete conversion to the exchange and jack program. The transponder tests will have been completed and by '80 a decision as to the city's meter reading conversion will have been made.

With decades of experience and modern technology, 'edmonton telephones' can be trusted to aid the community into the information age of the 1980s.

The Organization

A telephone company is made up of a lot more than telephone poles, instruments and a few thousand feet of wire. Almost 1800 people, with jobs ranging from clerk to general manager, work for 'edmonton telephones'. A variety of careers from engineer to operator, secretary to splicer, artist to accountant, and salesperson to switchman can be found in 'et'.

The organization is complex yet cohesive, ever-changing to accommodate new ideas and new technology. Jobs are eliminated and positions are created in an ongoing reorganization aimed at making the telephone department as effective and efficient as possible.

Throughout the city are spread miles of cable, hundreds of thousands of telephones, many types of customer communications equipment, millions of dollars worth of central office switching equipment, vehicles and departmental supplies. Personnel are scattered throughout the city, from the thirteen wire centres to downtown office buildings, warehouses, service centers and phone exchange stores — a total of twenty-four locations. All of those people and all the department's assets play an integral part in the organization that works as a team giving the best possible communications service to the citizens of Edmonton.

'edmonton telephones' is a distinct department of the city of Edmonton, as are Edmonton Power and Edmonton Water and Sanitation. The 'et' management is responsible to the city commissioners who are responsible to city council, members of which are elected by the people of Edmonton. Each taxpayer is therefore a shareholder in the city utility, as the profits of the utility are incorporated into city funds. Each subscriber benefits by a reduced mill rate, and a lower telephone rental.

Management positions at 'et' are ranked from Levels I to V. Level V is the position of general manager. The management belongs to CURA, an organization for all city management people. Other staff belong to either Local 1007 of the International Brotherhood of Electrical Workers (IBEW) or Local 52 of the Civic Service Union.

The general manager of 'et' is Mr. Ken Foster. Reporting directly to Mr. Foster are the managers of the five branches — chief engineer; general commercial manager; general plant manager; organization, development and financial results manager; and buildings, vehicles and supply manager — all ranked Level IV.

The engineering branch is headed by Harry Rogers, the chief engineer. Reporting to the chief engineer are five Level III section managers: equipment and building engineer supervisor, outside plant engineer, plant extension engineer, customer services engineer, and traffic engineering manager.

Gordon Lambe is the equipment and building engineer supervisor. This section is responsible for setting up central office equipment, which is the equipment inside the exchanges from the rack — a terminal point for cables — to the vast system of telephone switching equipment. The type, amount and operating characterisics of the central office switching equipment must be determined through extensive surveys and studies. The equipment is ordered and its installation is supervised by the department. when the system is in satisfactory working order, the equipment is then turned over to the plant department which handles operation and maintenance of the system.

If services adapt to accommodate the person sitting at home pressing buttons what hope is there for meaningful social intercourse? Gone will be the days of talking over the supermarket shelves, a cup of coffee in the office or a chance meeting on the street. we may have instant communication and information, but also instant alienation. Would we get to a point where man would be completely powerless against the machine and ruled by it? Would we lose our privacy and anonymity? The social implications are at once massive and frightening and exciting and welcome.

Perhaps interdependency is not all bad. We do need each other, not only for company but for survival. Today more than ever we are our brother's keeper. And what if we hadn't embraced the changes brought about by the industrial revolution. We would still be working long hours at backbreaking jobs and using the barter system in the marketplace. Who would want to go back to that type of life? Cannot the telecommunications industry be trusted to do its duty and maintain corporate responsiblity? Will the public know where to draw the line? TV phones were available ten years ago but the public rejected them. It's not necessarily true that donning garments of the wired world will turn us into unthinking and unmoving automatons.

Where does 'edmonton telephones' fit into the future technology. Edmonton has never been one to sit back and follow the actions of others. Since the 1880s when Alex Taylor installed the first phone system in Alberta and made the first long distance call in the west, Edmonton has been a leader in telecommunications. It was the first city in the west to consider and the second to install an automatic system, one of the first Canadian cities to initiate "911," computerized directory assistance, the CALRS program, and to install centrex sytems and transponders. In each case the change has been for the betterment of the industry and the community. certainly in the future 'edmonton telephones' will continue its tradition of leadership, always searching for ways to bring its customers the best telecommunications service available.

Three Level II engineers report to Mr. Lambe. Norville Robson, the transmission engineering supervisor, is responsible for the quality of connection from one phone to another, for ensuring customer electrical protection and for developing special circuit packages such as a hook-up between bank branches in different cities. This section is also responsible for establishing standards.

Mike Yakymyshyn is the equipment and building engineering supervisor. His group is responsible for emergency power in exchange buildings, construction and rearrangement of existing buildings and the acquisition of land.

Dale McIlhargey is the central office switching engineering supervisor. This section determines needs in central office equipment, orders it and oversees the installation. If the plant branch runs into a problem with the equipment once it is operational, this section helps overcome the difficulty.

A second section of engineering is the plant extension group headed by Ron Sollanych. Reporting to the plant extension engineer are three Level II employees: Roger Cucheran, engineering supervisor in planning; Jack Christensen, engineering supervisor for budgets; and Myron Solojuk, engineering supervisor in planning. This section co-ordinates the capital and current budget. it obtains city planning information from other city departments so it can identify where exchanges will be. The section conducts studies and surveys on the present system's requirements and capabilities. The studies also project the system's growth, in order to plan future needs for employees, plant facilities and buildings.

A third section of engineering is headed by Ray Goss, customer services engineer. Reporting to Mr. Goss are four Level II people: Dun Foster, building industry consultant service supervisor; Bert Yeudall, PBX engineering supervisor; Ken Parsons, key equipment engineering supervisor; and Tru Perry, radio engineering supervisor. This section handles customer requirements for large communications systems. This includes designing the physical layout, determining the capabilities of a system so it will meet customer requirements now and in the future, supervising the installation and making any needed adjustments.

A fourth section of engineering is outside plant engineering headed by William Dubik. Reporting to the outside plant engineer are four Level II employees: Joe Lukawesky, north area engineering supervisor; Don Glas, south area engineering supervisor; Roger Graff, outside plant staff engineering supervisor; and Ed Prior, plant location records supervisor.

This engineering section is responsible for all outside telephone equipment from the exchange rack to the home or office, including aerial, underground and buried cable. This group works with other city departments, and uses information supplied by plant extension to determine the most economical method of servicing new and existing areas. It estimates costs, prepares budgets, compares estimated with actual costs, and monitors total expenditure. It conducts periodic studies to see if engineering methods are up to date and comparable with other companies and reviews new products. It participates with government agencies in reviewing methods and procedures pertaining to safety standards in construction and maintenance of outside plant facilities. The group arranges the joint use of facilities with Edmonton Power, and co-ordinates joint construction. This section also keeps records of outside plant and equipment locations.

The last section of engineering is the traffic department supervised by Graham Barker. Reporting to Mr. Barker are three Level II personnel: Roy Lapp, traffic administration supervisor; Lary Samoil, traffic engineering supervisor; and Ken Armstrong, traffic supervisor.

Roy Lapp handles customer training and service analysis, data collection and systems support (which monitors for traffic measures and usage of central office and switching equipment), and dial assignments and methods.

Larry Samoil's group takes data from traffic administration and ascertains the switching equipment required, and engineers and designs inter-office trunking.

Ken Armstrong is in charge of directory assistance, which includes establishing "411" methods and training and supervising the operating staff.

A second branch is the commercial operation headed by Paul Trawick. Four Level III people report to the commercial manager: the director of business sales and service, the directory manager, the forecasting and methods manager, and the director of sales and marketing.

William Faist is the director of business sales and service. He has four level II personnel reporting to him.

Robert Kawchuk is the major market sales manager. He supervises five marketing consultants who handle large business orders. The consultants meet with the customer to discuss requirements and develop proposals according to customer requirements. The major account managers handle accounts such as the provincial and federal governments, the university, the city of Edmonton, and CN. These customers are contacted on a regular basis.

Robert Garnett is market sales manager handling the smaller companies and businesses. This group responds mainly to customer demand for telephone equipment. It consults with the client, orders equipment and monitors installation.

Eva Tutschek, a thirteen-year 'et' veteran, is a business sales and service unit manager. She has the distinction of being the only woman to achieve a Level II position in 'et', and one of a few in the city. Eva's section handles all demand telephone service other than special circuits. This includes individual business lines, key and switchboard accounts and major accounts. The section issues service orders, keeps records and handles pricing and payment. If a client is in arrears this group notifies him of the situation. Eva's section also notifies a customer if his number is going to change.

Wally Watt is the business sales and service unit manager handling all special requests, loops such as those connecting bank branches to a computer at central office, and data circuits which include fire and burglar alarms. The group also handles business and circuit account billings. The ISC co-ordinator in the section directs installations and is responsible for getting engineers to check standards. The equipment verifier checks to see if the equipment installed in businesses has been correctly recorded. The circuit supervisor directs the activities of ten service representatives. An administrative supervisor is in charge of the clerical personnel.

A second section of the commercial branch is the directory managed by Brian Holmes. Four Level II personnel report to the directory manager.

Bob Riley, the development, operations and research manager is in charge of all activities not directly related to the production of white and yellow pages. He handles the delivery of phone books and the investigation of new methods in directory production, such as new styles of ads.

George McFarlane is the yellow pages sales manager. He is in charge of two major-account sales representatives, the tel sel supervisor and salesmen who handle over-the-phone business, an eight-person sales force that handles smaller businesses, and two sales technicians who handle walk-in customers.

Jim Magee is the production manager. He supervises the artists, typesetters, the white pages compilation and the yellow pages compilation departments, and the Canadian National Yellow Page Service (CANYPS) that ensures that 'et' yellow page ads are distributed across Canada. The CANYPS department also receives yellow page information from other telcos in Canada. This section assembles the entire directory and sends it to the printers. In 1979 'et' will print about 500,000 books. About 70,000 will be sold to Alberta Government Telephones (AGT) to be distributed to neighboring toll free areas like Spruce Grove, and 25,000 will be sold to AGT to distribute to surrounding toll areas. The printer's bill for the 500,000 books will be about one million dollars.

Ed McDonald is the coin centre manager. He directs the ordering, installation, repair and maintenance of coin telephones and booths. He also supervises the coin location sales department and coin booth money collection.

A third section in the commercial branch is methods and forecasting. Reporting to the methods and forecasting manager are two Level II personnel. This department holds the honor of having the youngest staff in 'et' and one comprised mainly of university graduates.

Dave Rose is the director of commercial methods. This section conducts both long and short term studies to improve the economic efficiency of various aspects of the operations. Procedures such as the following have been examined: the handling of directory deliveries, for the purpose of making cost savings by improved efficiency in ordering, picking up and delivering directories; the preparation of a phone exchange manual containing the most up-to-date practices and procedures, for the purpose of standardizing the operation of phone exchanges to reduce the chance of error due to lack of knowledge and misrepresentation: and the development of a new deposit system for BSC, and aid in implementing it, for the purpose of assisting BSC in recovering monies that might have been lost from uncollectable accounts.

Yost Van Schaik is the forecasting supervisor. His group studies customer demands for all services, projecting 5 to 20 years into the future. This includes switch centre requirements and network facilities and types, and amounts of station apparatus needed, from residential up to large business establishments.

The last section in the commercial branch is sales and marketing under the direction of Brian Gibson. Reporting to Brian are five Level II people. Colin LeRougetel is the residential and business manager. Henry Zurch is business manager, special services. Jack McLean is the business and professional communications sales manager. Jack Laurie is the industry and technical sales manager. Bill Rothwell is the Phone Exchange manager.

This group initiates and develops new markets from large industries like Syncrude to smaller multi-line businesses. Once the market is established the group then turns the account over to the business sales and service section. The analytical sales group in this section, in co-operation with the customer services engineering group, determines if there is a market for certain equipment. The department also handles the administration of the phone exchanges.

A third major branch is plant, managed by general plant manager Fred Windwick. Reporting to Mr. Windwick are five Level III people: the director of distribution facilities, the director of repair, the director of customer taxation facilities, the director of switched network facilities, and the director of plant staff.

J. H. Young is the director of distribution. His section is in charge of installing all outside plant equipment such as underground, overhead and buried cable. Reporting to Mr. Young are four distribution facilities managers: William Ross in charge of the south telephone service centre; George Evans in charge of the west telephone service centre; Henry Lazarenko of the north telephone service centre; and Jim Burke at the north service centre, also in charge of maintenance. Also reporting to the director is plant, methods and results supervisor, Marvin Huffman. It is his duty to analyze new products in the field.

Pug Young is nationally recognized as running the best outside plant cable distribution system in all of Canada. Bell Canada tried to keep its cable troubles down to .5 per 100 stations. Pug's department is never over .14 per 100 stations.

A second section of the plant branch is headed by the director of repair, Alec Forbes. Reporting to Mr. Forbes are five production managers. Jack Tipping is in charge of phone conversion, which is converting all phones to the jack system. Gene Brenda is the PABX production manager, in charge of repair to this type of equipment. Al Mawhinney is in charge of business line and station key repair. Roy McBurney is in charge of repair of special services, like loops and circuits. John Protz is the test centre production manager.

This section handles customer complaints to the test desk. If the complaint or problem can't be cleared at the board, it is sent to the dispatch desk where repair crews can be assigned to make the repairs to the customer's phone or other equipment.

Steve Marusiak is the director of a third section of plant, the customer station facilities. There are five Level II personnel reporting to Mr. Marusiak. John Bogner, production manager, is in charge of line and station installations for central and south areas of Edmonton. Production manager Don Hunt is in charge of line and station installations for the north and satellite areas. John Wanchaluk is the key installations production manager for the central and south Edmonton areas. Ed Dawson is the key installation production manager for north and satellite areas. Gerry Lewis is the control centre production manager.

Stu Morrish is the director of a fourth section of the plant branch, the switched network facilities. In this department are approximately 180 craftsmen working in the various wire centres or exchanges in the city, including two female switchpersons, Gloria Hogweed at Strathcona and Ann Swist at the Lendrum wire centre. Reporting to Mr. Morrish are three managers — Doug Daugherty, Rod Small and Dave Anderson — each responsible for certain wire centres. The wire centre foremen report to these managers.

The last, newest and smallest section of the plant branch is the plant staff group set up in 1978 by Hap Elliott. Manager of plant staff is Ken Digweed. Reporting to Mr. Digweed are four Level II personnel. Ernie Kozak is in charge of the automated test centre or CALRS project, which stands for "customer automated loop reporting system". The system, scheduled for completion in 1979, will be installed in the main exchange building on 104 Street and 104 Avenue. The system is totally computerized. The computer will keep records of all trouble calls from city instruments. For instance, if the number 428-2020 is not working and the customer calls repair, a record of his complaints along with his name, address and information as to when the phone was repaired, or will be, would be fed into the computer. If that number experiences any more trouble the department will have a record of that telephone in the computer. This computer will also keep records of cable pairs.

John McMahon is in charge of major projects, most of which last from three to six months. These projects include evaluating measurements, productivity measurement and cost measurement.

Bob McLean is in charge of minor or short term projects. An example of a short term project could be a study on how installers report time when installing jacks and phones.

Graham Gale is the project manager responsible for staffing and budgets.

A fourth major branch in the telephone department is the organization, development and financial results branch, referred to as OD and FR. This branch is managed by Stan Shpiel.

Reporting to Mr. Shpiel are four Level III managers: the corporate planner; financial control and results manager; intercompany relations manager; and the director of training, safety and employment. This is another department with a high number of university graduates.

Howard Johnson is the corporate planner. Mr. Johnson's section studies the organizational structure and suggests changes to improve efficiency. An example of a recommended change would be to regroup the organization functionally, which could involve moving a multi-functional manager to a Level IV position. The planning section would also recommend changes such as the jacking system and the phone exchange concept. Three Level II people report to Mr. Johnson.

Jim Searle is the statistics and procedures manager. His section is responsible for data collection and input to plant cost and corporate methods.

Dave Goodall is the manager of business information systems. His group is responsible for co-ordinating the overall data processing activities of the department.

Doug McRae is the corporate studies supervisor. Doug's section handles depreciation rate development studies, and planning and economic studies.

A second section of OD and FR is financial results and control, managed by Tom Burns. Reporting to Tom are three men: Carlos Walli, Dan Check, and Bruce Zack.

Carlos Walli is the CATV cost accountant and is responsible for setting up monthly billing procedures to CATV companies for use of poles, ducts, pedestals and franchise charges. This section also conducts special studies: an example would be a survey on how many pocket pagers are in use. Other responsiblities are station equipment accounting by building location and aid in preparing the annual financial report.

Dan Check is the property and cost accounts supervisor. He is responsible for property and cost accounting, maintenance of property records and related investment in outside plant records. Dan is also involved with toll revenue studies.

Bruce Zack is the financial systems and budget officer. This section produces the monthly financial report, prepares and administers the budget, and takes care of general accounting and auditing functions of the department.

A third section of OD an FR is intercompany relations consisting of the manager Bruce Cleveley and Don Phillpotts. This section handles AGT, CATV, and 'et' intercompany agreements (which include toll revenues and connecting fees) and government agency and aldermanic inquiries, delegating them to various departments and reviewing the reports before they are passed on. The section also contracts with AGT regulatory bodies.

The last section of OD and FR is the personnel services section headed by Bob Hoy. Mr. Hoy handles 'et' manpower planning and labor relations. He is responsible for department administration and interpretation of applicable collective agreements. Mr. Hoy has seven people reporting to him.

Bruce Jessop is responsible for wage and salary administration. He must also maintain a system of departmental organization and employee records.

Ed Babych is responsible for administering the payroll section. He also administers the city-sponsored employee benefits to 'et' people.

Wally Bazylewich is in charge of the departmental safety policies and security for the company holdings. Wally's department handles building entrance security, annoyance calls to customers, and co-operates with the police department with regard to wire taps. Also included in this section is coin telephone fraud, unauthorized installation and general building security.

Another section of the department is management training. George Witt, along with Bob Johns and Roger Buzak are responsible for management training. They develop, evaluate, update and teach courses. They recommend courses offered within the community which would be useful for employees, and give orientation presentations to the new employees.

Roger Simkin is responsible for plant training, which includes training the various craftsmen like switchmen, installers and repairers. Roger must approve new courses and set objectives for general courses.

The last branch of 'edmonton telephones' was just organized by Hap Elliott, a 39-year Bell Canada veteran who came to 'et' in 1977 for a two-year period to set up the plant staff section and buildings, vehicles and supplies branch (BV and S).

Mr. Elliott is currently the manager of BV and S. This section combines groups previously with the plant section and the OD and FR section.

Reporting to the general manager of BV and S is the administrative service director, Al Josey. Mr. Josey is responsible for space studies, user interface on space, and user request. He determines requirements and building locations, and interacts with engineering people.

Also reporting to the manager is the director of buildings, vehicles and supplies, Don Hunt. Don has four Level II people reporting to him.

The project manager of BV and S handles furniture, building maintenance, vehicle functions and budgeting.

The material manager, Don Hlady, is in charge of supplies from telephone sets and switchboards to cables. Don's group keeps track of supplies. When supplies of a certain item are low, the city univac computer and the mini computer at Main notify the staff.

Also reporting to the director of BV and S are repair shop managers Cliff Allen and Don Parks.

Cliff Allen's section is in charge of the radio shop located in the communications building by the CN Tower. The radio shop personnel do repairs on two-way radios, and service pocket pagers and portable radios. The electronics or PABX shop handles repairs on electronic secretaries, pay phones, voy call, and outside and central office plant testing equipment. It repairs and rebuilds PABX packages, refurbishes PBX packages, builds electronic paging systems and builds special apparatus for PBX and PABX equipment.

Don Park's department includes several technical repair shops: a shop for the repair of telephone sets; the carpentry shop which builds tables, desks or chairs needed in the organization; the paint shop which repaints phones; and the Mopeco engine shop which handles repairs on power tools and the heaters used in manholes.

This is a very general and simplistic outline of the 'et' organization. It was not taken below the managerial Level II, as it would be impossible and impractical to describe the structure in minute detail. Also the very nature of the organization — always changing — would soon make much of the information outdated.

The Wired World of the 1980's

There is a computer bank of medical knowledge in the States which can be tapped instantly by almost any doctor in the world, helping to diagnose and cure diseases. The facsimile industry is talking about a new way of sending letters — by machine instead of the postal system. In Chicago, phone calls, data and video signals are being transmitted on pulses of light in hair-thin glass fibres. Telephone companies are installing a new digital switching system that takes up only one-quarter of the space now in use. The telecommunications industry is dreaming of another totally new and as yet unknown discovery that will revolutionize the industry again perhaps in ten years. It is also engaged in a search for a method of transmission that doesn't require an actual physical joining between outside plant and inside switching equipment. The dreams of the wired world of 1984 are no longer just dreams. We have the technology. The age of information is here.

Fibre optics is a term presently on the tip of everyone's tongue. Although the concept is not new, it has just recently proven itself in field tests. The idea has been around for a hundred years. In 1880, Alexander Graham Bell received a patent for a telephone called a "photophone" which transmitteed calls by light instead of along wire. The sound of Bell's voice was carried on a beam of sunlight. He had a great idea, but he didn't have the technology to make it work. Beams of light were disrupted by fog, air, clouds and rain, and the photophone wouldn't work at night. It wasn't until 1957 that the laser was utilized, and twenty years later that it used fibres of very thin glass as its transmitting medium. Bell laboratories, the leader in the field of fibre optics, has devised a detector which converts more than half of the light power coming through one glass fibre to electrical energy which in turn is converted to sound energy to ring the telephone. This detector can detect incoming light signals at one frequency and transmit signals at another frequency. This allows sending and receiving signals over one glass fibre with just one device.

Fibre optics is a tremendous improvement over copper cable in space requirements and cost. One hair-thin glass fibre can carry the same number of messages as a 1200-pair copper cable, and it is said that if the copper could be taken out of the cable and sold it would pay for fibre optics. Fibre optics is being used in a number of places in North America under different test conditions. It is thought that problems will be encountered with glass in extreme weather conditions such as sub-zero temperatures. One CATV company in southern Ontario is presently experimenting with fibre optics aerially and will hopefully discover the effect of ice, snow, wind and other conditions upon the glass.

Once fibre optics proves itself, 'et' will probably install it in new areas and possibly do conversions on a large scale.

Digital switching, the latest method of transmitting signals, has a future in telecommunications which looks very promising. In digital switching, or time and phase division multiplex, random samples of the conversation are picked up. The analog voice pattern is scrambled, changed to a mathematical pattern, sent over the line, and unscrambled at the other end. If a person could cut in on the line of a digital transmission, he would not be able to understand the conversation. The machine doesn't transmit the actual voice, but transmits a reproduction of the conversation. DMS is based on the theory that in a normal conversation a lot of time is wasted in pauses between words and sentences, and so a lot of machine time is also wasted. Also, it is not necessary for the machine to hear the total word to know what that word is. The computer can be programmed to fill in the gaps and to condense the conversation. This saves time and money when the conversation is transmitted.

There are many advantages to the digital switching system. It is about one-quarter of the size of cross-bar and SP1. It requires less space to operate in and less space to be manufactured in. This results in significant savings from lower building and utility costs and reduced land and maintenance costs. If Edmonton were to switch completely to digital, only one-quarter of the space in the present wires centres would be used. There would be no need to spend more money on land, building materials, utilities and wages. The wire centres in use now could accommodate expansion for many years to come. The cost savings would be enormous once the initial conversion expenses were paid.

Digital systems are more reliable and in many cases easier to service because of the compactness of the component parts. Again significant savings would be realized in maintenance and personnel — not to mention a more satisfied public. The digital is also more versatile than the analog system. It can carry voice, data, signals and high fidelity and it can transmit with fewer distortions.

It's quite certain that 'et' will be installing digital systems, but probably not in the next ten years because the equipment now in use is adequate. The telephone or telecommunications industry has grown by evolution rather than revolution. It has changed slowly from one system to another, and now that DMS is here, companies won't immediately junk cross-bar and SP1. Probably step-by-step will be replaced by DMS.

The speed at which conversion takes place will depend on the point at which costs are equalized, that is, where the costs of conversion equal the cost savings that result. The present line may be 25 or 50 percent. If it is found, in a number of years, that it would be more economical to switch entirely, then that's what 'et' will do. On the other hand, the digital system may be replaced by a newer system within ten years. Technology is moving so fast now that almost as soon as a new system is discovered, scientists are already theorizing and experimenting with newer systems. Since another revolutionary new transmission system is expected to make its appearance in about ten years, it might be advisable not to switch completely to digital. A new system could be so totally different that everything in the telephone network would be obsolete. A new system might necessitate a change all the way from switching equipment to customer equipment.

Western Union is introducing digital systems and the company expects to be converted entirely by 1981. Xerox is proposing a totally digital communications network and has applied to the FCC to get space in the 10 GH band. Digital is definitely here for now, and in the following few years will find home in many telcos across the country.

Another system that has been around for years but hasn't been feasible for widespred use until now is Q-Fax or facsimile service. Q-Fax was available in 1920, but then it was too costly and too slow. Today the service has improved to a state where it is within economic range of the customer. It is being looked upon as an alternative to the postal system. A letter still may take five days to get from one coast to the other, but a facsimile machine in Vancouver could send words and pictures to another machine in Halifax in one day. This would be a boon to businesses that rely on quick and efficient transmission of information.

Perhaps the most exciting work in telecommunications now is the search for a means of transmission that would eliminate the actual physical connection between the outside cable and the inside central office switching equipment. This would remove the rack — the large frame that joins thousands of cable pairs to the inside switching equipent. No matter how small the digital equipment inside and fibre optics equipment outside, the telco still needs a huge building to house the rack — the frame or connection point. Laboratories across North America are now in the process of finding a way to connect the inside to the outside without that physical connection. Perhaps a system could be perfected where a laser projected from the inside would scan and transmit data from the cable ends.

Another change in telcos in North America in the next few years will be the complete change to a marketing-oriented industry in order to compete with large facsimile and interconnect companies. Telcos will offer a wide range of services and equipment to customers and, if run efficiently, the telco will be able to offer these services at the best cost. Telcos will have to maintain strict cost and inventory control in order to remain competitive.

The 'et' department, during the past twelve years, has been changing direction and attitude. It has become a market-oriented department and has worked to maintain a good image in the community. 'edmonton telephones' should be able to hold its ground against other industry-related competitors.

There are many new products already on the market or just over the horizon. AGT has just made audio-video conference calling available between Edmonton and Calgary. A roomful of people in Calgary can have a conference with a roomful of people in Edmonton for under $200 an hour, a cost significantly less than the price of six or seven air-bus fares. Home computers are available which, as well as answering your telephone, will record and send messages, turn lights and appliances off and on at set times, monitor the house for theft and smoke and maybe act as a wake-up service. A person could leave their house knowing that if something unexpected happened the computer would automatically call the neighbors or police and play a pre-recorded message asking for assistance.

In the future a person will be able to dial a number on the telephone, be connected to any data bank to access any information, and through an interface connected to the telephone and a cathode ray tube (TV) see the information on the screen. A person could get basic information like weather, news and race results by dialling one number and could get more specialized information from any number of proliferous and accessible data banks anywhere in the world.

Scribble phones would be common. In this a phone call to a data bank, say the Centennial Library, could allow you and an associate some distance away to read the same page in a book, edit it on the screen with a light pencil, press a button and have the document retyped to your specifications.

The data bank and access system could lead to a totally different lifestyle. The home and office, in many cases, would become one and the same. A person could work out of his home, accessing various people and sources of information from his home system. A great many duties could be done via the video-audio system. Lanes of the supermarkets could be viewed on the screen and selections could be made by pressing a button. The items would be delivered to your door and the bill would be sent to your bank where your account would be debited to the amount of the bill. All banking and shopping could be done at home. Businesses would change to accommodate the system. Standing at a wicket in the bank would be a thing of the past, so would waiting in line at the supermarket, so would robbing the grocery store. Schools could be conducted over local television, eliminating large building and transportation costs. Instead of buying a newspaper, you would just switch to a news channel where you could access any news story or in-depth article. Dogs wouldn't be able to bite postmen as most of them (postmen) would be eliminated, nor could they chase cars all day as movement would be minimal. If a person was not in his home he could access information through his wrist watch, or a two-way beeper. Some people believe that briefcase mobile phones in cars will be standard by 1985. This would result in frequency congestion even worse than that caused by the CB craze. We might need licenses to use the phone if the department of communications didn't devise new rules.

The wired world is very exciting and very controversial. There are those who argue that instant accessibiity to all forms of services and information will stifle our creativity and turn us into brainless and incapable robots. The calculator adds, subtracts, multiplies and divides. It's fast, easy and costs only $16. Why learn mathematics? But what does a person do if he's out of batteries and can't find an AC outlet? Why go to university and wear out the books if any piece of information is only as far away as your telephone? Why go out to see a friend if you can visit over the phone? Why go to the gym for a game of ball if you can play it with a video game attachment on your TV. Why learn to bake, sew or fix your car when a machine can do it for you. In the case of an energy shortage, how many would freeze to death or starve to death, not from lack of wood or flour, but from lack of knowledge and skills.

If services adapt to accommodate the person sitting at home pressing buttons what hope is there for meaningful social intercourse? Gone will be the days of talking over the supermarket shelves, a cup of coffee in the office or a chance meeting on the street. We may have instant communication and information, but also instant alienation. Would we get to a point where man would be completely powerless against the machine and ruled by it? Would we lose our privacy and anonymity? The social implications are at once massive and frightening and exciting and welcome.

Perhaps interdependency is not all bad. We do need each other, not only for company but for survival. Today more than ever we are our brother's keeper. And what if we hadn't embraced the changes brought about by the industrial revolution. We would still be working long hours at backbreaking jobs and using the barter system in the marketplace. Who would want to go back to that type of life? Cannot the telecommunications industry be trusted to do its duty and maintain corporate responsiblity? Will the public know where to draw the line? TV phones were available ten years ago but the public rejected them. It's not necessarily true that donning garments of the wired world will turn us into unthinking and unmoving automatons.

Where does 'edmonton telephones' fit into the future technology. Edmonton has never been one to sit back and follow the actions of others. Since the 1880s when Alex Taylor installed the first phone system in Alberta and made the first long distance call in the west, Edmonton has been a leader in telecommunications. It was the first city in the west to consider and the second to install an automatic system, one of the first Canadian cities to initiate "911," computerized directory assistance, the CALRS program, and to install centrex sytems and transponders. In each case the change has been for the betterment of the industry and the community. Certainly in the future 'edmonton telephones' will continue its tradition of leadership, always searching for ways to bring its customers the best telecommunications service available.

Acknowledgements

The main sources of information for this history came from the pages of the *Edmonton Bulletin* and the *Edmonton Journal*. Many long hours were spent on the microfilm machines at the Centennial Library reading the *Bulletin* issues from 1880 to 1914 inclusive and other issues to 1950. More hours were spent on the machines in the library of the *Journal*, reading selected articles from 1936 to 1978. I was allowed access to the town and city council meeting minutes and selected files at City Hall. More information was gathered from city clerk files, EDTC files, *Bulletin* and *Journal* telephone files, Henderson Directories, City of Edmonton reports, personal and miscellaneous files at the City Archives and sessional reports at the Centennial Library. Other sources of information included the Provincial Archives at the Museum, the Saskatchewan Archives at the University of Regina, and the Bell Archives in Montreal.

A great deal of information was gathered from present and past 'et' employees, and individuals associated with the company and industry; more came from 'et' files, "The Communicator" and "Telephone Topics."

Thanks to the second floor staff of the Centennial Library, the *Journal* library staff, the City Archives staff and the City Hall records staff; Tony Cashman for access to some research material and Jack Horley for collecting material and photographs. Special thanks to Dunc Foster, Al Forbes, Pug Young and Al Eager who allowed me to pick their brains on many occasions and many thanks to the 'et' executive — Ken Foster, Paul Trawick, Fred Windwick, Harry Rogers, Stan Shpiel and Hap Elliott.

Bibliography

Cashman, Tony. *Singing Wires*. Edmonton: 1972.

Collins, Robert. *A Voice From Afar*. Toronto: McGraw-Hill Ryerson Ltd., 1977.

Communications News. Annual Forecast Issue. (January 1979)

Jamieson, Col F.C., V.D.Q.C. " Edmonton Courts and Lawyers in Territorial Times." *Alberta Historical Review,* IV (Winter, 1956).

MacDonald, J.S. "The Dominion Telegraph." *Canadian Northwest Historical Society Publications,* Volume I, Number VI, (1930).

MacGregor, J.G. *Edmonton, A History*. Edmonton: M.G. Hurtig, 1967.

Ream, Peter T. *The Fort On The Saskatchewan*. Second Edition. Metropolitan Printing. 1974.

Ronaghan, Allen. "The Telegraph Line to Edmonton." *Alberta Historical Review,* (Autumn 1970).

Scientific American. (November 1978) p. 131.

"Uncomplicating Telephone Company Security." *Telephony,* (November 24, 1975), pp. 24-25.